DOMEBO

**CONTRIBUTIONS OF THE
MUSEUM OF THE
GREAT PLAINS**   Number 1

PUBLISHED IN LAWTON, OKLAHOMA
BY THE
GREAT PLAINS HISTORICAL ASSOCIATION

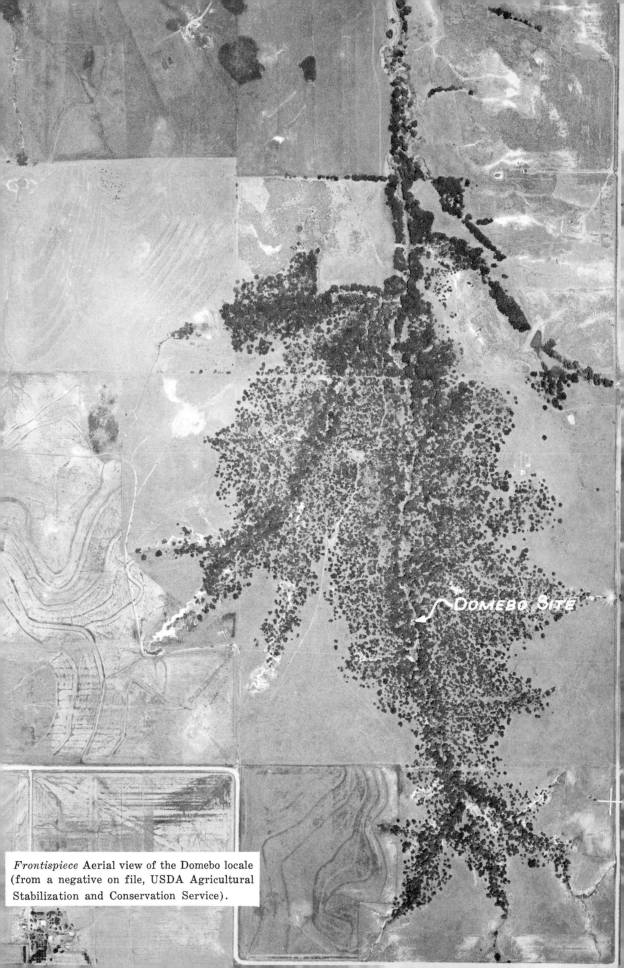

DOMEBO SITE

Frontispiece Aerial view of the Domebo locale
(from a negative on file, USDA Agricultural
Stabilization and Conservation Service).

DOMEBO:

A Paleo-Indian
Mammoth
Kill in the
Prairie-Plains

Edited by FRANK C. LEONHARDY

Published as
Contributions of the Museum of the Great Plains,
Number 1
Lawton, Oklahoma
1966

To Glen L. Evans, geologist,
we dedicate this report
as a measure of appreciation
for his contributions
to our knowledge
of the Paleo-Indian.

Research at the Domebo Site was supported
by two grants from the National Science Foundation
NSF-G22002
Recovery of Paleo-Indian Cultural Remains
and
GS-132
Pleistocene Ecology of the Domebo Mammoth Site

Library of Congress Catalog Card Number: 65-26284
PRINTED IN U.S.A.

EDITOR

PREFACE

A note on format: The symposium was considered to be the only reasonable format for publishing the results of the Domebo investigations. In this way each of the investigators receives due credit for his efforts. Each investigator presents his own data and conclusions in an independent paper, so there is some redundancy in matters of general information. Because many of the authors will circulate their papers as offprints, this information has been retained.

There is presently a rumor afoot which I am loath to acknowledge but which I feel should be dispelled in print. The rumor is that the projectile points found at the Domebo site were planted. This is false, but the situation which gave rise to the rumor was an unfortunate one. A visitor who was in no way connected with the project placed several projectile points of Archaic style in the Pleistocene deposits downstream from the excavation and then arranged for their discovery by himself. He later confessed his misdeed. No reasonable doubt can be placed on the association of the projectile points and skeletal material found in the excavation at Domebo, and the two independent "discoveries" should not be confused.

The number of people who aided the Domebo project is so great that to list them all would require as much type as any one paper. To those who remain unnamed, our sincere and grateful "Thank You." Some of those to whom we owe particular gratitude are: Mr. J. E. "Buck" Patterson and his family for reporting the site and for their hospitality to all who worked there; Kirby Smith and Virgil Oaks for their aid, interest and hospitality; the Tri-County Well Service and the Shelton Construction Co. for the use of their equipment.

The Anadarko Area Office of the Bureau of Indian Affairs supported the project administratively, morally and physically. This assistance is truly appreciated for without it the site could not have been excavated. And, without the financial assistance from the National Science Foundation, excavation would have been, at best, difficult.

To the heirs of the estate of Mr. Charlie Domebo we acknowledge our debt in the traditional manner of archaeology by naming the site after the Domebo family. *Ah-ho*.

The crew who moved the muck and the overburden were Lee McNair, Franklin Chappabitty, Donald Kwakala and Lloyd Heminoke. Adrian Anderson was the archaeologist-in-charge.

For radiocarbon dating we acknowledge the services of the following laboratories and individuals: the Radiocarbon Dating Laboratory of Kaman Instrument Corporation (formerly Texas Bio-Nuclear) and Russell Kinningham; the Socony Mobil Oil Company Field Research Laboratory and E. E. Bray; The Division of Radiation and Organisms of the Smithsonian Institution and Austin Long; Geochronology Laboratories of the University of Arizona and Vance Haynes; the USDA Agricultural Research Service and L. L. McDowell and Coyde Yost. Theirs were particulary valuable contributions.

Mrs. Suzanne Burgess aided with some of the artifact illustrations; Mrs. Janet McGee and Mrs. Lucille Leonhardy did the bulk of the clerical work connected with the production of the report.

I would like to thank Vance Haynes for a number of things, especially for processing the bone fractions for radiocarbon dating and for writing his paper on the age and dispersion of fluted projectile points. The many investigators and several independent reviewers have kept check on my use of both fact and conclusion, but I include the usual caution that they are in no way responsible for any of my errors. ⋀

Frank Leonhardy
Lawton, Oklahoma
October, 1965

TABLE OF CONTENTS

LIST OF FIGURES

LIST OF TABLES

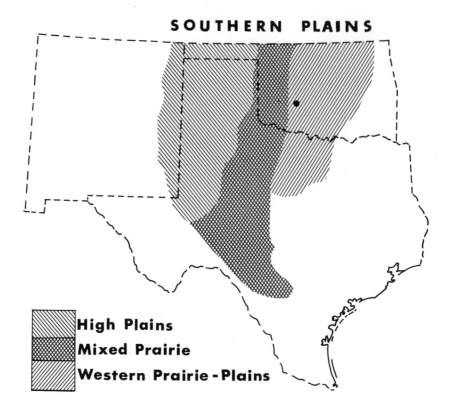

SOUTHERN PLAINS

High Plains
Mixed Prairie
Western Prairie-Plains

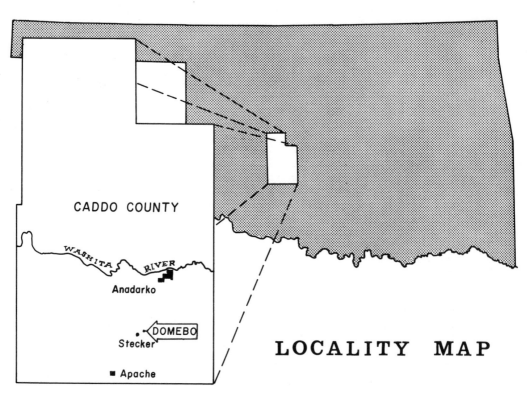

CADDO COUNTY

WASHITA RIVER

Anadarko

DOMEBO

Stecker

Apache

LOCALITY MAP

FIG. 2

INTRODUCTION

domebo (Kiowa: dó m • bâ, locally anglicized to *duḿ bo*) bugle, flute or flagolet.

This is a report on the interdisciplinary investigations at Domebo, a Paleo-Indian mammoth kill site in the Prairie-Plains of southwestern Oklahoma. These investigations were a coordinated effort to obtain as much data as possible about the culture of the hunters of the Domebo mammoth and the environment in which they lived. The report consists of eight separate papers, each dealing with a major aspect of the investigations. While any one paper might stand alone as a contribution to a scientific discipline, the report is intended as a single, unified study.

The Domebo site was first reported to the Museum of the Great Plains in December, 1961. Adrian D. Anderson, then the museum's Curator of History and Anthropology, visited the site with the discoverer, Mr. J. E. "Buck" Patterson of Apache, Oklahoma. There he found portions of mammoth skull, tusk and vertebrae exposed in a deposit of fine, bluish-grey silt. The exposure was in the bank of a spring-fed stream at the bottom of a deep, narrow ravine. Mr. Patterson stated that the tusk had been exposed for a year or more, protruding from a natural dam. When heavy rains destroyed the dam, other skeletal material was exposed.

Anderson returned to the site and began exploratory investigations to determine the possibility of a human association and the feasibility of excavation. While cutting a channel beside two articulated vertebrae to divert the stream, a medial fragment of a projectile point was found. The artifact was below water level, so its location was not observed prior to removing it. It was, however, found in the distinctive blue silt surrounding the bone and was close to the two vertebrae. The discovery of an artifact under conditions suggesting direct association with mammoth remains prompted the invitation of a number of archaeologists and geologists to visit the site. Those who responded were Dr. Robert E. Bell, Department of Anthropology, University of Oklahoma; Dr. William J. Mayer-Oakes, then director of the Stovall Museum, University of Oklahoma; Dr. David Kitts, Department of Geology, University of Oklahoma, and Dr. Jeremiah Epstein, Department of Anthropology, University of Texas. All agreed that in view of the discovery of the fragmetary projectile point, the site warranted extensive excavation.

With evidence of a possible man-mammoth association in hand, arrangements for excavation began: The National Science Foundation made an emergency grant to help defray the cost of excavation; the Anadarko Area Office of the Bureau of Indian Affairs processed the application for an excavation permit from the Department of the Interior; the myriad of lesser details were dispatched and excavation began on February 1, 1962.

The Domebo project did not begin as quite the extensive project it became. Initially only geological and archaeological studies were planned, but Dr. Claude Albritton recognized the potential information available in the geological deposits and suggested that his colleagues, Dr. Elmer Cheatum and Bob Slaughter, be contacted. Dr. Retallick and Dr. Mehl had already consented to aid the project; Dr. Wilson later agreed to undertake paleobotanical studies at the site. Each of these gentlemen visited the site at one time or another during the course of excavation. With each visit the scope of the project grew. The National Science Foundation awarded a second grant which financed the ecological studies at the site and which provided for a symposium on the Domebo investigations. Most of the investigators met at the Museum of the Great Plains in May, 1963, to discuss their findings, compare notes and resolve differences of opinion. The following papers are a result of that conference.

FIG. 3   Bone exposed in the west bank of Domebo Branch, December, 1961.

FIG. 4   View of the site about midway in the course of excavation. View is to the south from the west bank of Domebo Branch.

2

GEOMORPHOLOGY
OF THE DOMEBO SITE

Harold J. Retallick

THE DOMEBO SITE is located in a deep, arroyo-like branch of Tonkawa Creek about three miles east of the village of Stecker and six miles northwest of Cyril. The legal description of the site is NE¼, SW¼, SE¼, Sec. 29, T6N, R10W, Town of Tonkawa, Caddo County, Oklahoma. The name "Domebo Branch" is suggested for that tributary of Tonkawa Creek on which the site is located. Domebo Branch, though not so named on maps, can be located on both the 15- and 7½- minute Apache Quadrangles of the USGS topographic map series.

The writer considers the locale of the Domebo site to be on the eastern margin of the Great Plains. No attempt will be made to conform with the definition of the eastern margin as presented by Fenneman (1938:616-619) and Atwood (1940, Pl.6), both of whom place this part of Oklahoma in the Central Lowlands province. Curtis and Ham (1957) on their "Physiographic Map of Oklahoma" place most of Caddo County in a Western Sandstone Hills region, a region similar in its eastern outline to the Gypsum Hills of the Osage Plains (Fenneman 1938, Figs. 174; 617). The classic works of Marbut (1923, Figs. 1; 44) and Shantz (1923, Figs. 1; 83) include this region within the limits of the Great Plains. More recently, geographers have tended to include this part of Oklahoma within the Great Plains (Zakrzewska 1963; Griffin, Young, and Chatham 1962; Miller, Parkins, and Hudgins 1954).

TOPOGRAPHY

Generally speaking, the Domebo locale lies in an undulating plains region where local relief is largely determined by the type of outcropping material from Permian "red beds" of the Rush Springs and Cloud Chief Formations.

The mammoth kill site, which is on the headwaters of the Domebo Branch of Tonkawa Creek, is situated close to a gypsum-capped divide between north and south flowing drainage systems (Fig. 5). Streams to the south of the divide are bordered by both undulating and hilly land. They have established normal dendritic patterns and have produced smooth and moderately broken features of relief. North of the divide the minor features of the topography are strikingly different. Tributaries of Tonkawa Creek, such as Domebo Branch, descend from the divide in steep channels. The scoring of the soft sandstone of the Rush Springs Formation and Quaternary or Recent deposits has produced rugged arroyos and intricate minor badland erosion features.

West of the Domebo locale the topography is typical of the rolling plains of western Oklahoma. The terrain to the east, however, is entirely different. Here butte-like outliers of the Cloud Chief Formation cap a narrow drainage divide between the north and south flowing systems.

TONKAWA CREEK

Stream profiles, valley cross sections and entrenchment through alluvial fills along Domebo Branch are similar to those found along other drainage systems that emerge from the upland south of the Washita River. For example, Delaware Creek and Tony Hollow Creek, five and eleven miles east of the Domebo locale, have depositional and erosional features strikingly similar to those of the Tonkawa Creek system.

Tonkawa Creek and its tributaries drain an area of approximately forty square miles of upland on the south side of the Washita River.

Tonkawa Creek rises in the center of the Cement oilfield and follows a northerly course for about four miles. Here the valley is narrow, V-shaped and confined by north-projecting ridges capped by the Cloud Chief Formation. Once the course is fully established in the softer Rush Springs Formation, the valley broadens

3

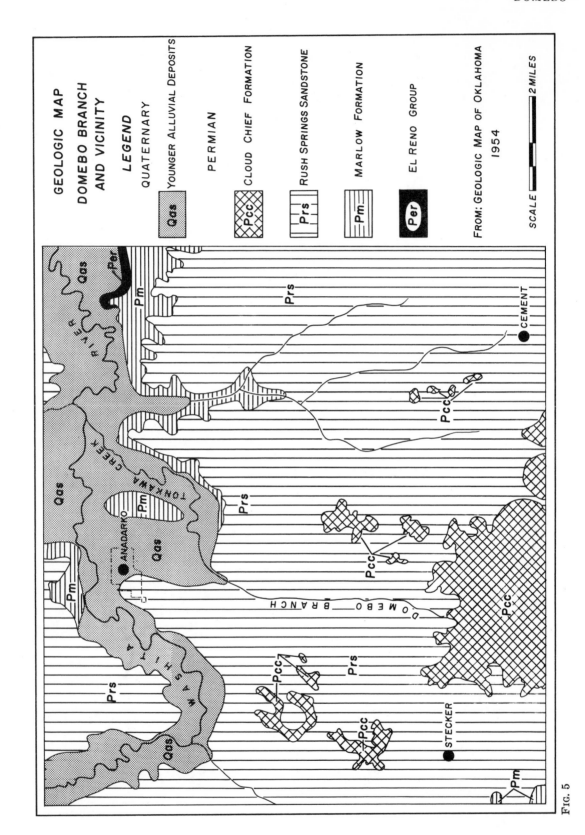

GEOLOGIC MAP
DOMEBO BRANCH AND VICINITY

LEGEND

QUATERNARY

Qas YOUNGER ALLUVIAL DEPOSITS

PERMIAN

Pcc CLOUD CHIEF FORMATION

Prs RUSH SPRINGS SANDSTONE

Pm MARLOW FORMATION

Per EL RENO GROUP

FROM: GEOLOGIC MAP OF OKLAHOMA 1954

SCALE 2 MILES

FIG. 5

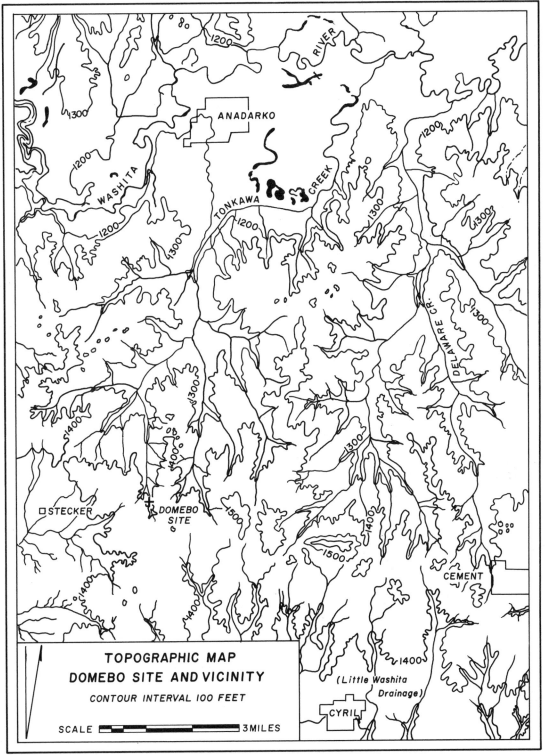

TOPOGRAPHIC MAP
DOMEBO SITE AND VICINITY

CONTOUR INTERVAL 100 FEET

SCALE ▭▭▭▭ 3 MILES

FIG. 6 Topography and drainage pattern of Domebo site and vicinity based on USGS Anadarko, Apache, Cement and Fort Cobb quadrangles.

5

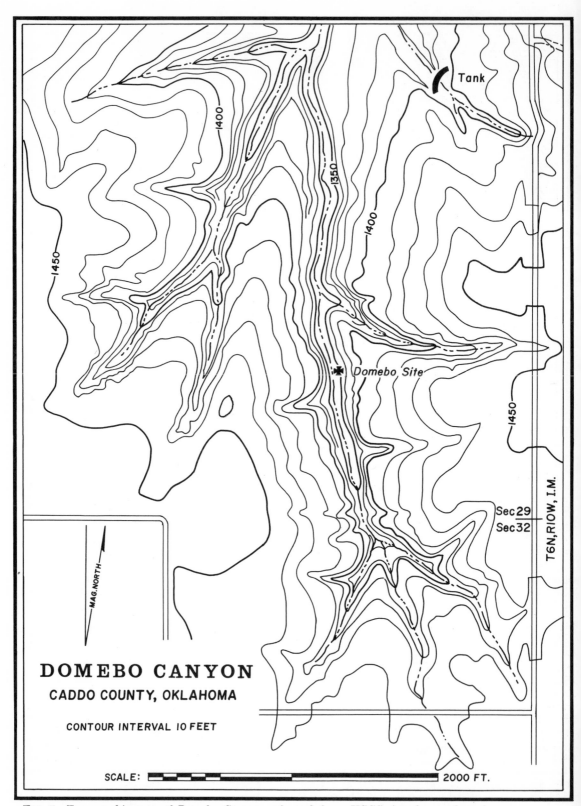

Tank

1400

1350

1400

1450

1450

Domebo Site

Sec 29
Sec 32

T 6N, R10W, I.M.

MAG. NORTH

DOMEBO CANYON

CADDO COUNTY, OKLAHOMA

CONTOUR INTERVAL 10 FEET

SCALE: ▭▭▭▭▭▭▭ 2000 FT.

FIG. 7 Topographic map of Domebo Canyon enlarged from USGS Apache quadrangle.

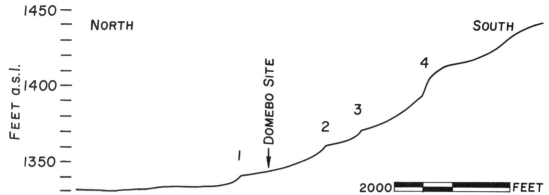

FIG. 8 Longitudinal profile of Domebo Branch from Chicago, Rock Island and Pacific Railroad bridge to open fields at the head of the tributaries which form the branch.

and the creek turns westward for about a mile. On resuming a northward course and picking up western tributaries, it is confined to a slightly narrower valley until it emerges onto the Washita River floodplain. Tonkawa Creek breaks from the uplands about two miles south of Anadarko. Its northeasterly course across the floodplain of the Washita follows a former course of the master stream. Terraces are easily recognized and seem to conform with those described by Ross (1962: 159-163).

A reconnaissance of Tonkawa Creek and its western tributaries was made by walking the tracks of the Chicago, Rock Island and Pacific Railroad tracks from the Washita River floodplain to the railroad bridge at the point where Domebo Branch enters the system. Of special interest along the course of the traverse was the valley form. Almost without exception, the valley cross section shows a wide, flaring, smoothed slope beginning about seventy feet above the valley bottom. Lower slopes were steep. This characteristic valley form is similar in profile to Domebo Branch (Fig. 9). Along the entire traverse there was ample evidence of the presence of a terrace pattern. However, many of the terraces were either partially or totally destroyed by construction of the railroad.

DOMEBO BRANCH

Two profiles, a longitudinal type along Domebo Branch and a vertical cross section of the valley fifty feet south of the site, were surveyed. The longitudinal profile was surveyed between the Chicago, Rock Island and Pacific Railroad bridge in the center of Sec. 17, T6N, R10W and a major headwater gully of the branch in the NE¼, Sec. 32, T6N, R10W. An Abney level on a 5-foot Jacob staff was used for vertical measurements. Horizontal distances were paced. A transit and stadia rod were used in the survey of the cross section of Domebo Branch (Dr. H. Lee Hoover of Springfield, Missouri, assisted). Three elevation control points were established along Domebo Branch by transit traverse from two U. S. Geological Survey bench marks, one at an elevation of 1335 feet, located in the northeast corner of Sec. 20, T6N, R10W, and the other at 1485 feet in the NE¼, SE¼, SE¼, Sec. 32, T6N, R10W.

The longitudinal survey of Domebo Branch (Fig. 8) brought to light three interesting breaks or interruptions of slope. If these interruptions in the profile represent nick points, they might infer more than one cycle of erosion as advocated by Penck (Davis 1922: 587-598) or as independently developed by Meyerhoff and Hubbell (1928: 315-381). However, among American geologists, nick points in the profiles of streams are usually considered to be the expression of an ungraded situation. As such, they might be explained in terms of varying rock resistance, mass wasting of valley slopes or aggradation by overloaded tributaries. According to the doctrine of Penck, these explanations might be inadequate and the possibility that nick points represent interruptions in the profile as the headwater limits are extended after periods of intermittent uplift should not be dismissed. The writer would interpret the interruptions in the profile as evidence of cyclic uplift, but a more exhaustive survey and study would be required to establish this point.

In Figure 8 nick point No. 1 is at an out-

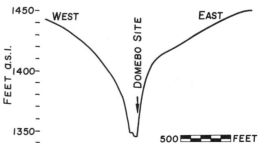

FIG. 9 Profile of Domebo Canyon fifty feet south of the Domebo site.

crop of Rush Springs sandstone about 500 feet downstream from the Domebo site. Because of a limited exposure, no conclusive evidence as to the relation of the resistance of the sandstone in the outcrop to adjacent layers could be obtained. The terraces seem to pinch out at the nick point, but since there was considerable slumping of recent alluvial material it would be dangerous to regard this interval as evidence of a distinct cycle of erosion.

The interruption in profile at nick point No. 2 was produced by a temporary dam of large trees and slump debris from the east valley wall. A small pond impounded behind the dam was filled with alluvium and humic material. Again, no conclusive evidence which would indicate cyclic uplift was gained.

A good exposure of rather homogeneous Rush Springs Sandstone is present at nick point No. 3. Former plunge pools eroded in sandstone are scattered along the course of the branch to the headwall at nick point No. 4. Nick point No. 3 offers a chance for conjecture that it might be the result of cyclic uplift. If such uplifts did occur, there must be more evidence available on the flanks of the Wichita Mountains.

The cross section of Domebo Branch (Fig. 9) is typical of the profile of many streams that flow from the gypsum-capped ridges northward into the Washita River. All tend to exhibit an upper convex, or waxing, slope. Along Tonkawa Creek and the Domebo Branch, the smooth upper slope is approximately seventy feet above the valley floor. Sand dunes are common features of the upper slope area. The lower valley walls tend to be steep with some free faces of sandstone outcrop, a considerable amount of detrital material and some residual material. Scattered remnants of terraces are in evidence.

Once the cycles of aggradation and degradation of the Pleistocene were completed, streams in the region entered a period of active downcutting. Whether or not downcutting was due to cyclic uplift of the whole region or was controlled by erosion cycles of the Washita River could not be readily determined. However, the last cycle of erosion began in historical times. Discussions with Mr. W. K. Smith of Route 3, Stecker, Oklahoma, and several other older residents who live in the locale of the Domebo site confirmed this belief. All mentioned that the branch had cut down some ten or more feet in the last thirty years. Since the depth of the present valley of Domebo Creek is fairly uniform from its lower reaches to the mammoth site, waters for entrenchment and retreat of the gully-head are probably from accelerated run-off at the headwaters.

An interesting aspect of the present valley floor of Domebo Canyon is the presence of potholes and debris-dammed basins. One such basin, above the Domebo site, was investigated. Measurements were made to determine depth to the rock floor. At a number of points the floor could not be reached with a six-foot soil auger. A subsequent plot of the depth measurements showed that the alluvial material was at least three feet deep on the average and over six feet deep in what must have been a former stream channel. Removel of part of the debris dam lowered the water level about 18 inches. In the alluvial material exposed by partial drainage, there was some evidence of stratification of sand, silt, and organic material (mostly leaves). The mire-like condition prevented a detailed investigation, but led to the conjecture: Could a similar condition have existed on Domebo branch at the time of the mammoth kill?

At the time of the deposition of the Domebo Formation, the branch stream was probably at, or very close to, the level of the Washita River. Therefore, Domebo Branch could have been an embayment of the master stream, at least during periods of high water. It is here postulated that the lower member of the Domebo Formation was deposited when the physical environment was suitable for the deposition of a clayey deposit. A lowering of the master stream could have removed the marsh condition by permitting drainage of the branch to proceed normally. The sandy upper member of the Domebo Formation, which is probably from the sandstone outcrops of the Rush Springs Formation, could have been derived through weathering and deposited by rill erosion. The identical process is in operation today in Domebo Canyon and its tributaries.

It should be noted that the erosional and depositional history appears to be the same in canyons and gullies adjacent to Domebo Branch. The canyon immediately east of Domebo Branch was investigated and a formation very similar to the Domebo was found under the heavy overburden of later Quarternary deposits. Present day erosion is proceeding in the same manner as in Domebo Canyon. Identical pothole and debris-damned pools are present.

Conditions are favorable for the discovery of other elephant sites, especially if the early hunters operated in this area for any period of time. Early man, as a hunter, could have used the box canyons such as Domebo and their sections of soft alluvium to his advantage. If a mammoth were driven into Domebo Canyon from the larger river bottoms to the north, the animal would perhaps be in such a state of exhaustion and frenzy that it might have become mired in the shallow alluvium. ⋀

REFERENCES CITED

ATWOOD, W. W.
1940 *The Physiographic Provinces of North America.* Ginn and Company, Boston.

CURTIS, N. M. AND W. E. HAM
1957 Physiographic Map of Oklahoma. Oklahoma Geological Survey, Norman.

DAVIS, W. M.
1922 Peneplains and the Geographic Cycle. *Bulletin of the Geological Society of America,* No. 23, pp. 587-598. New York.

FENNEMAN, N. M.
1938 *Physiography of the Eastern United States.* McGraw-Hill Company, New York.

GRIFFIN, P. F., R. N. YOUNG AND R. L. CHATHAM
1962 *Anglo-America: A Regional Geography of the United States and Canada.* Fearon Publishers, San Francisco.

MARBUT, C. F.
1923 Soils of the Great Plains. *Annals of the Association of American Geographers,* Vol. 13, No. 2, pp. 41-67. Albany.

MEYERHOFF, H. A., AND M. HUBBELL
1928 The Erosional Landforms of Eastern and Central Vermont. *Annual Report of the Vermont State Geologist,* 1927-1928, pp. 315-381. Montpeilier.

MILLER, G. J., A. E. PARKINS AND BERT HUDGINS
1954 *Geography of North America.* Wiley and Sons, New York.

MISER, H. D.
1954 Geologic Map of Oklahoma. Oklahoma Geological Survey, Norman.

ROSS, A. R.
1962 The Washita River, A Preliminary Report. *Proceedings of the Oklahoma Academy of Science,* Vol. 42, pp. 159-163. Norman.

SHANTZ, H. L.
1923 The Natural Vegetation of the Great Plains. *Annals of the Association of American Geographers,* Vol. 13, No. 2, pp. 81-107. Albany.

ZAKRZEWSKA, BARBARA
1963 An Analysis of Landforms in a part of the Central Great Plains. *Annals of the Association of American Geographers,* Vol. 53, No. 4, pp. 536-569. Lawrence.

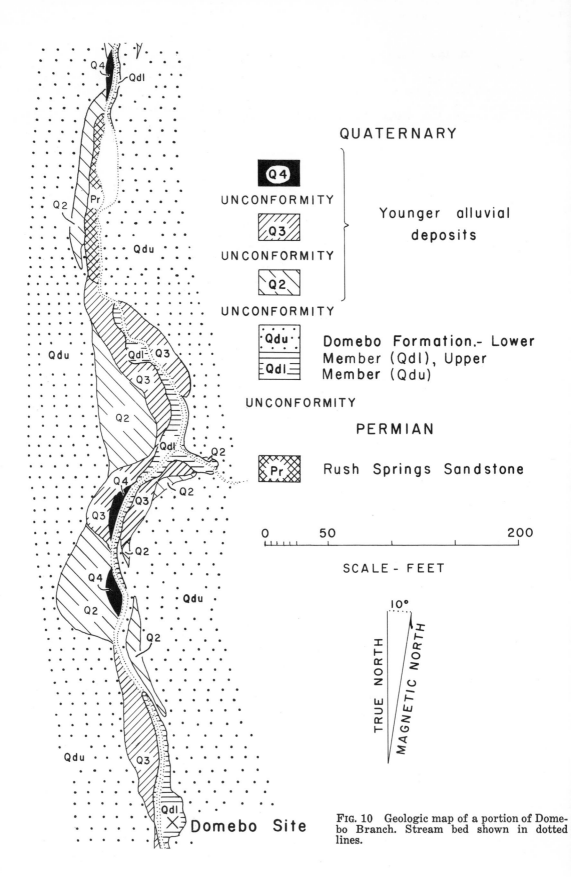

QUATERNARY

Q4

UNCONFORMITY

Q3

UNCONFORMITY

Q2

UNCONFORMITY

} Younger alluvial deposits

Qdu
Qdl

Domebo Formation.- Lower Member (Qdl), Upper Member (Qdu)

UNCONFORMITY

PERMIAN

Pr

Rush Springs Sandstone

0   50   200

SCALE - FEET

10°

TRUE NORTH   MAGNETIC NORTH

Domebo Site

Fig. 10 Geologic map of a portion of Domebo Branch. Stream bed shown in dotted lines.

STRATIGRAPHY OF THE DOMEBO SITE

Claude C. Albritton, Jr.

THE HEADWATER GULLIES of Domebo Branch are entrenched in Permian "red beds" of the Rush Springs and Cloud Chief Formations. Downstream from the confluence of these gullies, four benches of Quaternary alluvium rise in steps of 2, 7, 14 and 40 feet above the bed of the stream. The alluvium of the highest bench, containing the elephant bones and associated artifacts which are the subject of this symposium, is here named the Domebo Formation. Three bodies of younger alluvium, which fill nested channels cut into the Domebo Formation, are informally designated as Q-2, Q-3, and Q-4, in order of decreasing age. Figure 10 shows the pattern of the alluvial deposits, Figure 11 their structural relationships.

RUSH SPRINGS SANDSTONE

About 500 feet downstream from the Domebo Site, the Rush Springs Sandstone crops out along the bed of the creek. Here the sandstone is a massive and friable rock, consisting mostly of fine, angular grains of quartz, which are loosely bound together by a reddish ferruginous cement. Because the cement is unevenly distributed, the sandstone is variegated in color, ranging between light brown and very pale orange.

The Rush Springs Sandstone is the principal source of the Quaternary alluvial deposits in the area. Like its parent material, the alluvium is predominantly fine textured and, except where masked by humic materials, retains in varying degrees the brownish cast of the Permian red beds.

DOMEBO FORMATION

The type section of the Domebo Formation was measured on the steep eastern bank of the creek at the Domebo site. The sequence is divided into two parts, informally called the lower and upper members.

TYPE SECTION OF THE DOMEBO FORMATION

	Thickness (Feet)
Upper Member	
6. Silt, clayey and sandy; pale yellowish brown; massive or in alternating darker and lighter layers several inches thick; flecked with whitish films and pellets of calcium carbonate.	16.3
------------Local disconformity------------	
5. Sand, fine, silty; light brown; mostly of angular quartz grains, with scattered rounded grains in medium grade range; contains lentils of clay pellets; bands of grayish humic sand in lower foot.	7.0
------------Local disconformity------------	
4. Sand, fine; grayish orange; mostly of clear angular quartz grains; interbedded with grayish humic and silty sand; bedding surfaces generally subparallel:wavy, lenticular or irregular in detail.	7.2
3. Sand, fine; yellowish gray; mostly of clear angular quartz grains; interbedded with gray sand in units an inch or less thick.	1.5
Lower Member	
2. Silt, clayey, humic; olive gray; sandy toward top; contains abundant snail shells.	3.8
1. Sand, tan; contains lentils of brownish clayey silt. Exposed in pit at Domebo Site. Total thickness unknown.	3.8+
Total exposed thickness	39.6

Lower Member—The base of the Domebo Formation was not exposed in the archaeological excavations at the type locality. Farther downstream, however, the dark clayey silt of Unit 2 laps over the Permian bedrock and there forms the basal unit of the formation. While it is clear that the Domebo alluvium fills a channel cut into the Rush Springs Formation, the dimensions and course of this ancient valley are not known.

Unit 2 is the only part of the Domebo Formation that can be traced for any considerable distance. Below the site it crops out in many places in the bed and along the lower banks of the creek. Farther northward, beyond the limits of the area covered by the geological map, it forms small riffles and falls. Several lines of evidence suggest that Unit 2 is a fossil paludal soil. The clayey silt owes its dark color to abundant and finely dispersed organic matter. It contains numerous shells of snails, mostly of species which today inhabit marshy and swampy areas.

About 100 feet downstream from the site, two sizable tree trunks were found rooted in the dark silt, their tops covered by cross-laminated sand of the upper member. One of these stumps yielded a radiocarbon date of 11,045±647 B.P.; a sample of lignitic wood found in the excavation dated 10,123±280 B. P. These dates would place the lower member near the close of the Pleistocene Wisconsin Stage.

Upper Member—At the type locality, the upper member rests conformably upon the Lower Member and is intergradational with it. Near the base of the upper unit, lentils of dark humic silt are interbedded with yellowish-gray sand. Humic lentils are less common at higher horizons, and except in the modern soil zone near its top, the upper member is relatively free of organic matter.

In general, the upper member is fine-textured and either massive or evenly bedded. Locally the sequence is interrupted by disconformities, marking places where channels were cut and later filled. The depth of these buried channels ranges upward to five feet. Thin beds of pebble and cobble gravel line some of the deeper cuts, and contorted beds along the sides show where the channels were partially filled by slumping.

YOUNGER ALLUVIAL DEPOSITS

Q-2 Alluvium—This body of alluvium forms discontinuous benches which stand about 14 feet above the bed of the creek. The Q-2 unit rests upon an erosional surface developed upon the Domebo Formation and the Rush Springs Sandstone. In most places this is a surface of disconformity, but near the inner margins of the benches there is commonly an angular discordance between the bedding of the Q-2 and the Domebo.

The following section, measured at the northern margin of the area shown in Figure 10 is characteristic of this unit.

Section of the Q-2 Alluvium

Thickness
(Feet)

4. Sand, fine; pale yellowish-brown; mostly of angular grains of clear quartz; massive or cross-laminated on small scale; three-foot soil zone at top has white films and pellets of calcium carbonate at base.   9.0

3. Gravel; granules, pebbles and cobbles of brown sandstone, gray sandy clay and milky quartz set in sandy matrix; contains abundant bones of *Bison* sp.   1.0

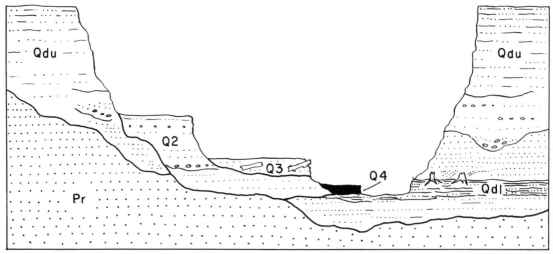

FIG. 11 Diagrammatic cross section of Domebo Branch. Pr—Rush Springs Formation; Qdl and Qdu —lower and upper members of the Domebo Formation; Q2, Q3, Q4—younger alluvial deposits.

----------------Local disconformity--------------------
2. Sand, fine; grayish orange; mostly of angular to sub-rounded grains of clear quartz; grades into Unit 1.   2.5
1. Sand, fine; light brown; mostly of angular to sub-rounded grains of clear quartz; massive; contains bits of lignitized wood. Base not exposed.   2.0

Total exposed thickness   14.5

Q-3 *Alluvium*—Narrow and discontinuous benches, which stand about seven feet above the bed of the stream, are floored with two to four feet of alluvium. The base of the Q-3 unit is a surface of erosion developed on the Domebo Formation and Q-2 unit.

About 350 feet north of the site, the Q-3 unit contains a raft of tree trunks and branches. Beneath the bark the wood is soft and rotten, but the stage of decomposition has not advanced beyond what one would expect to find in dead timber exposed for a decade or so on the floor of a forest. The wood is set in a matrix of grayish-orange fine quartz sand, finely laminated at some horizons and cross-laminated at others.

Q-4 *Alluvium*—This unit caps small marshy benches which are only about two feet higher than the bed of the creek. A trench dug into one of these benches, 175 feet north of the site, exposed pale yellowish-brown clayey and silty fine sand. The alluvium contains abundant leaves and stems of plants.

HISTORICAL SUMMARY

Before eleven thousand years ago, near the close of the Wisconsin Stage of the Pleistocene, alluvium began to accumulate along a gully carved in the Rush Springs Sandstone. At first the bed of the stream was uneven, and the more level stretches were marshy. In the marshy reaches the dark silt of the lower Domebo Formation accumulated. The bones of a mammoth, killed by hunters who left some of their spear points in the carcass, were buried beneath these deposits.

After the channel of the stream had become more evenly graded, the marshes were covered with layers of fine sand, reworked from the Rush Springs Sandstone. In time a floodplain was established at a level upwards of 40 feet above the former bed of the creek.

Domebo Branch has subsequently entrenched itself to a depth near that of its original channel, establishing partial or incipient floodplains at the upper faces of the Q-2, Q-3, and Q-4 alluvial bodies in the process. The entrenchment continues, and the valley is being widened by mass wasting.

Far-ranging stratigraphic correlations are probably premature, but it is interesting to note that the radiocarbon dates of *ca.* 11,000 B. P. for the lower part of the Domebo Formation is comparable with dates of *ca.* 11,000 and 9500 B. P. recently obtained for the Sulphur River Formation of Delta County, Texas (Slaughter and Hoover 1963). Both formations are related to tributaries of the Red River. Doering (1963), in turn, correlates the Sulphur River Formation with the Prairie Formation in the Red River terrace sequence, and with the Holloway Prairie Formation of the Gulf Coastal Plain.

REFERENCES CITED

DOERING, JOHN
    1963   Correlation of the Sulphur River Formation. *Journal of the Graduate Research Center*, Vol. 31, No. 3, pp 149-151. Dallas.
SLAUGHTER, BOB H. AND B. REED HOOVER
    1963   The Sulphur River Formation and the Pleistocene Mammals of the Ben Franklin Local Fauna. *Journal of the Graduate Research Center*, Vol. 31 No. 3, pp 132-148. Dallas.

THE ARCHAEOLOGY
OF THE DOMEBO SITE

Frank C. Leonhardy and
Adrian D. Anderson

THE DOMEBO SITE, registered as Cd-50 in the Oklahoma Site Survey Files, is located at the bottom of one of the many steep-walled gullies cut into the rolling Prairie-Plains country of southwestern Oklahoma. Throughout this region small streams have cut deeply into the Permian sandstone bedrock, creating canyons which, in more recent geologic times, have been filled with alluvium and then recut, forming narrow gouges in an otherwise monotonous topography. These ravines are seldom more than two hundred feet across, but from brink to bottom their banks may drop fifty or sixty feet. Their borders are heavy with growths of cedar, cottonwood, elm and oak; the narrow bottoms are thick with brush, reeds, grass and debris fallen from above.

The mammoth remains were found on the east side of Domebo Branch, under a slight knoll at the bottom of a bank which sloped upwards at an angle approaching ninety degrees. Opposite the bone bed, and immediately downstream was a small terrace standing four feet above the creek; from the terrace the west bank rose steeply upward to the top of the ravine.

EXCAVATION PROCEDURE

The bone bed was the primary unit of excavation since it constituted a single archaeological feature within a discreet geological formation. Horizontal control within the excavation was maintained through a quadrant-grid system; vertical control was maintained with a transit set at an arbitrary elevation.

After preparation of surface profiles, squares on the west bank were excavated to facilitate diversion of the stream; then the slump deposits on the east bank were removed. When fully exposed over the initial area of excavation, the blue silt unit was removed with trowels. As each bone was exposed, its position relative to the control system was recorded and

photographs and drawings were made; it was then jacketed and removed. The waterlogged condition of both bone and fill left the bone extremely fragile and the pedestals unstable. This, coupled with nightly freezing, made removing the bone from the excavation as soon as possible expedient. Moreover, there was a distinct possibility of a sudden thaw or rain: Either would have destroyed the excavation.

All of the bone in the deposit was east of the original exposure and excavation eastward produced an increasingly unstable wall. An area of the face fifty feet wide was cleared of loose earth and a series of step-like faces were prepared. The final eastern limit of excavation was reached when the bank had been cut to the point of instability. Three weeks after work ceased, the site was buried by slumping.

STRATIGRAPHY

In this paper the essential concern with stratigraphy is with the position of the bone bed in the lower member of the Domebo Formation and with evidence for disturbances in the bone bed (Figs. 12; 13). Albritton's more inclusive description of stratigraphy is presented elsewhere in this symposium. Although the Domebo Formation is composed of a complex series of superimposed and interdigitated alluvial deposits, the stratigraphy within the excavation was relatively simple:

A. *Recent Slump Deposits.*

Recent slump covered the area of the bone bed. In most instances the slump rested upon an eroded surface of the lower member, but in the area of the skull it intruded the bone bed. This deposit was derived from the upper member, but it contained an admixture of recent alluvium and organic debris. Maximum thickness of the deposit was three feet.

B. *Upper Member of the Domebo Formation.*

The upper member was thirty-two feet thick at the site. It constituted the major overburden and was cut back ten feet in the excavation area.

C. *Lower Member of the Domebo Formation.*

The organic material in the lower member gives it a distinctive color which varies from black through light blue, hence the informal names "blue clay," "black silt" or "blue silt." The unit is principally a slack water, or marsh, deposit consisting of discontinuous, interdigitating bands of sand, silt and clay. It is an aquifer, and the groundwater imposed a serious handicap to excavation. Much of this member had been eroded away in the area above the bone bed; when encountered, the boundary with the upper member was four feet above the level of the skeleton. The total thickness of the member is unknown, but only the top five feet are of immediate interest. Three units were associated with the bone (Fig. 16):

C1. *Tenacious Brown Clay.*

A band of fine brown clay, varying in thickness from one to six inches, was uniformly "draped" over the bone bed. In those areas where they protruded through the underlying grey sand, the bones were covered by the brown clay.

C2. *Grey Sand.*

Fine, light grey sand surrounded the skeleton, although much of the bone protruded through it. Thickness of the unit was variable, ranging from one or two inches to a foot or more.

C3. *Olive Drab Clayey-Silt.*

A very thin, slightly cemented band of dark clayey-silt which may have been a dry ground surface was uniformly distributed throughout the excavated area. The band was penetrated only by the tusk; the rest of the bone almost invariably rested directly upon it. No evidence of disturbance could be found, so the ground must have been reasonably solid when the animal died.

The bone bed was at least twice disturbed by erosion. The more recent disturbance (Z_2) cut into the bone bed and destroyed half of the skull and mandible. This erosion was temporarily averted by a slump which the stream later cut through, leaving the bone re-exposed (Z_3). An earlier stream movement, near the end of the deposition of the "blue clay," cut into the bed and removed an unknown number of skeletal elements (Z_1). The bottom of the channel then filled with gravel. The left femur was partially uncovered by this stream action and subsequently covered with gravel; the proximal femoral epiphysis and one phalanx were found in the gravel close by. A piece of a right ilium of mammoth, probably a part of the Domebo skeleton, was found forty feet down-

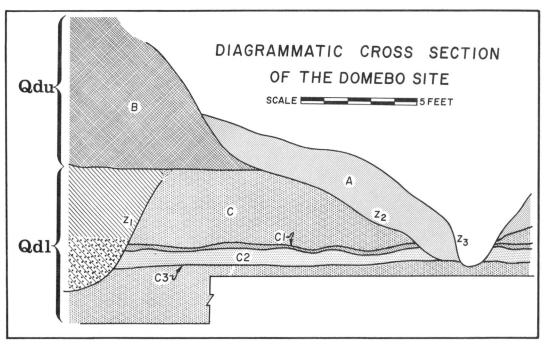

FIG. 12 Diagrammatic cross section of the stratigraphy in the Domebo excavations. A—recent slump deposits; B—upper member of the Domebo Formation; C—lower member of the Domebo Formation; C1—tenacious brown clay; C2—grey sand; C3—olive drab clayey silt; Z_1, Z_2, Z_3—erosional features.

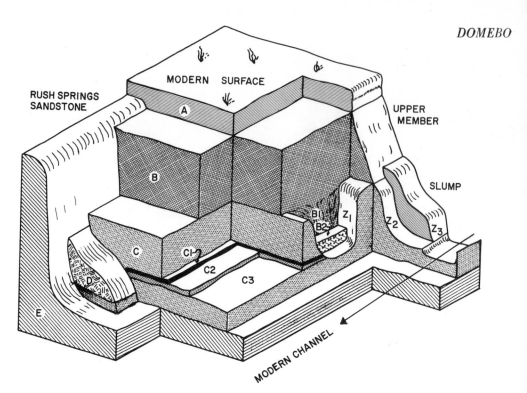

Fig. 13 Isometric diagram showing relationship of geologic units in Domebo Canyon at the Domebo site. Considerable license has been taken with scale and actual position of units. A—modern surface and soil development; B—Qdu; C—Qdl; C—brown clay; C2—grey sand; C3—olive drab clayey silt; D—brown clay inlier; E—Rush Springs sandstone; Z_1, Z_2, Z_3—erosional features. Relationship of D to E hypothetical.

stream, resting on blue silt but covered with gravel.

Immediately upstream from the site was an inlier of brown sandy-clay which apparently had been a bank of the marsh which was covered by the contained deposits. One of the three tree stumps found in the lower member was rooted in this material.

The stratigraphic evidence suggests that the mammoth died on solid ground. Shortly thereafter the ground was flooded and the remains were partially covered with fine sand. The water did not recede, but instead remained as a pond. Fine clay particles settled from the water, completely covering and sealing the bone bed.

Bone Distribution

The mammoth originally lay on its left side with the head to the north and the hindquarters to the southeast (Fig. 14). The forelimbs were disarticulated, but reasonably close together. In a few instances vertebrae were associated in a manner suggesting articulation, but for the most part they were scattered in a narrow band between the skull and the sacrum. One femur lay south of the pelvis; the other femur and the one tibia recovered were with the bones of the forelimbs. The left scapula had vertebrae and ribs resting upon it. The glenoid

fossa section of the right scapula had been removed, but much of the remainder was found. Of the teeth, only one molar was recovered in the excavation; one had been removed from the exposed mandible by the discoverer and two others were found in the stream bed. All four molars in occlusion at the time of death were recovered, as were numerous plates of immature molars.

All prepared bone was closely examined in the laboratory for such evidence of butchering as cut or hack marks. None was found. The distribution of bone within the site, particularly the dispersal of the large leg elements, and such unnatural associations as a rib beneath the pelvis can be interpreted as the result of butchering. The small particle size of the deposits around the bone indicates that the force of the water which deposited them probably would not have been sufficient to move bones as large as a mammoth femur.

The Artifacts
DESCRIPTION

Two projectile points, a medial fragment of a projectile point and three unmodified waste flakes constitute the entire artifact assemblage recovered with the skeleton. Descriptions of three additional artifacts found in the stream bed are included in this report because there is some

16

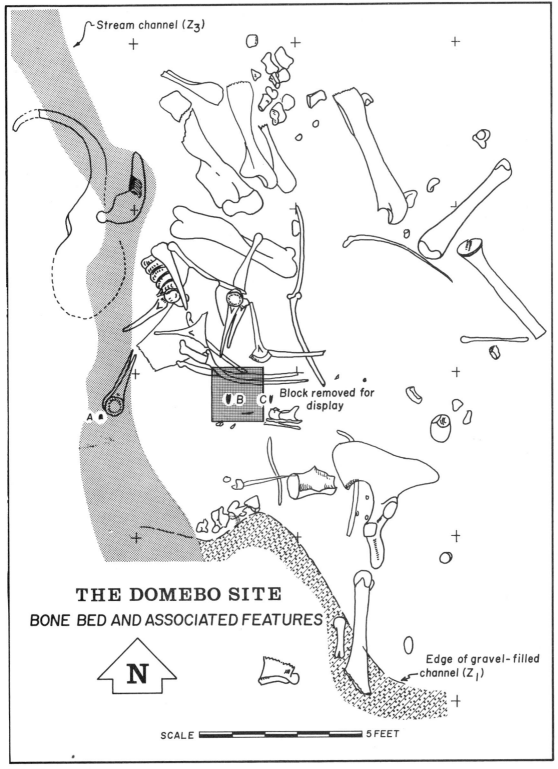

Stream channel (Z₃)

Block removed for display

A

B   C

THE DOMEBO SITE
BONE BED AND ASSOCIATED FEATURES

N

Edge of gravel-filled
channel (Z₁)

SCALE   5 FEET

FIG. 14

Fig. 15   The Domebo excavations near completion. The boundary of the upper and lower members of the Domebo Formation shows at the top of the photograph.

reason to believe that they may have been originally associated with the site.

Except for the one projectile point found in the stream bed, the artifacts are made of an extremely fine chert similar to that found in the Edwards Limestone Formation of central Texas. Samples of tabular chert collected near Round Rock, Texas, compare favorably with the material of the Domebo artifacts. The color of this chert is generally a dark blue-black, although lighter colors, such as tan, light blue and light grey occur. The two flake scrapers retain a brownish-white cortical patination.

A. *Medial fragment of a projectile point, MGP catalog 64.8.1 (Fig. 19a).*

A medial fragment of a projectile point was found in the bank of Domebo Branch near two vertebrae during the initial reconnaissance of the site (Fig. 14A). It is 41 mm. long; 22.5 mm. wide at the proximal end and 12 mm. wide at the distal end; the maximum thickness is 7 mm. On the proximal end of the obverse face is

a large flake scar, but this is not the remnant of a flute for it has been cut by transverse flakes. The color of the artifact is a light blue-grey with inclusions of dark blue-black.

B. *Projectile point, MGP catalog 64.8.2 (Fig. 19b).*

The first point found *in situ*, this artifact was in an area of disarticulated ribs and vertebrae (Figs. 14B; 17). The extreme tip of the specimen is broken. It is 78 mm. long; maximum width is 28 mm.; width at the base is 24 mm.; maximum thickness is 7 mm. The base is concave, 2 mm. deep; the sides are slightly convex. Basal grinding extends 27 mm. up one edge and 31 mm. up the other.

The major flute scar is 34 mm. long and a maximum of 21 mm. wide. A second, deeply grooved, flake scar adjacent to the flute represents an additional, subsequent, attempt to thin the base. The reverse face is not fluted. A large flake scar near the base of this face is a remnant of an early step in the manufacture of

FIG. 16   Geologic *units related to the bone bed show* in the block to the right of the pelvis. A—brown clay; B—grey sand; C—olive drab clayey silt. Projectile point "C" found near vertebrae in lower right corner.

the point, for it is cut by flakes removed laterally from the edge. The color of the point ranges from a medium blue-grey through blue-black. The tip has a brownish cast.

C. *Projectile point, MGP catalog 64.8.3 (Fig. 19c).*

The second point found *in situ* was near a pair of articulated vertebrae (Figs. 14C; 18). The length of the point is 68 mm.; the maximum width is 21 mm.; the width at the base is 19 mm. The base is concave, 2 mm. deep; the sides are parallel at the proximal end. Basal grinding extends 22 mm. up either edge.

The obverse face of this point has been basally thinned by removal of four parallel flakes. The longest of these, and the last to be removed, is 23 mm. long and 5 mm. wide; a second long flake is 14 mm. long and 4 mm. wide. On either side of these is the remnant of a much shorter flake scar. The reverse face has a

short flute 20 mm. long, 10 mm. wide at the proximal end and 6 mm. wide at the distal end. Adjacent to the flute is the remnant of a prior flake 7 mm. long and 4 mm. wide.

D. *Projectile point, MGP catalog 64.9.2 (Fig. 20).*

A fourth projectile point was found in gravel downstream from the excavation. Except for the material from which it is made, a fine-grained quartzite, it closely resembles the points from the site both in terms of style and technology; its more crude appearance is a function of material, not workmanship.

The tip and one corner of the base are missing. The length is 57 mm.; maximum width is 24 mm.; approximate width at the base is 22 mm.; maximum thickness is 10 mm. The base is concave, about 2 mm. deep; the sides are convex. Basal grinding extends 22 mm. up either edge.

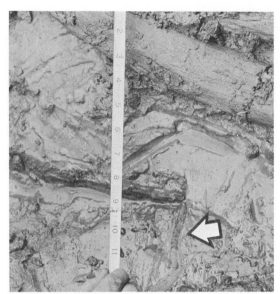

FIG. 17 Projectile point "B" (64.8.2) *in situ* four inches from mammoth rib.

One side exhibits a well defined thinning flake, 17 mm. long and 9 mm. wide, which terminates in a hinge fracture. Removal of this flake has obscured the scars of two, or perhaps three, prior flakes removed from the base. The other side has two parallel flake scars, one 13 mm. long and 5 mm. wide; the other 10 mm. long and 5 mm. wide. Both terminate in hinge fractures.

To re-emphasize, this point was not found in the excavation, but is included in this report because it was found near the excavation and because it bears a strong typological resemblance to the points found with the skeleton.

E. *Flake scraper, MGP catalog 64.9.1 (Fig. 21a)*.

A unifacially flaked side scraper made on a blade of the same blue-black chert from which the points are made was found in stream gravels some ten yards downstream from the excavation. Two bits of evidence suggest that it may have been associated with the site. The material from which it is made is virtually identical to that of the points: Of the several flakes found in the stream bed, only this and the one described below are of the same distinctive chert as the points. Second, the gravels in which it was found are the same as, or at least derived from, the gravels associated with the Z_1 channels on the south edge of the bone bed.

The artifact is 67 mm. long; the maximum width is 32 mm.; the maximuum thickness is 9 mm. The cross section is generally triangular. Two edges have been unifacially flaked to form a cutting or scraping edge. Most of the bulb of percussion is present, but the striking platform has been removed. The edges have been heavily used.

F. *Worked flake, MGP catalog 64.9.3 (Fig. 21b)*.

Another large worked flake was also found in the gravels downstream from the excavation. It, too, is of the same chert as the points; the only noticeable difference is in the slight brownish cast to the color. For the same reason mentioned above, this artifact originally could have been associated with the bone bed.

The length of the artifact is 60 mm.; the maximum width is 41 mm.; the maximum thickness is 9 mm. The cross section is triangular. Two edges have been unifacially retouched to form cutting edges; both show wear. The flake has been broken laterally, so neither the bulb of percussion nor the striking platform is present.

G. *Unmodified waste flakes*.

Three small waste flakes of the same chert as the projectile points were found in the bone bed. These are of some importance for they are certain evidence that someone was either making or reshaping tools on the site after the death of the animal.

DISCUSSION

The two complete projectile points present something of a typological problem, for one—the smaller—is as reminiscent of the Plainview type as it is of the Clovis type. Similarities between these types have long been noted. Krieger (*in* Sellards, Evans, Meade and Krieger 1947), in the type description of the Plainview material, noted some resemblances, but at that time he was more concerned with ambiguities in the

FIG. 18 Projectile point "C" (64.8.3) *in situ* near lower thoracic vertebrae.

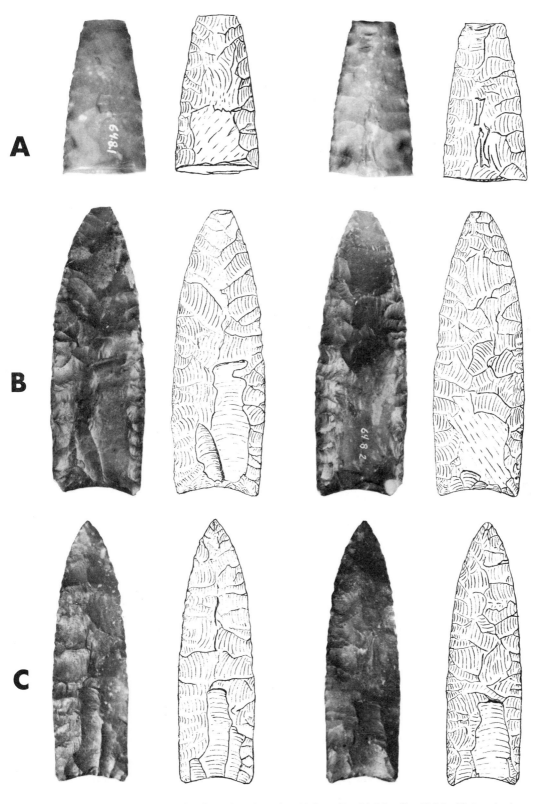

FIG. 19   Projectile points from the Domebo site.   A—64.8.1;   B—64.8.2;   C—64.8.3.   Natural size.

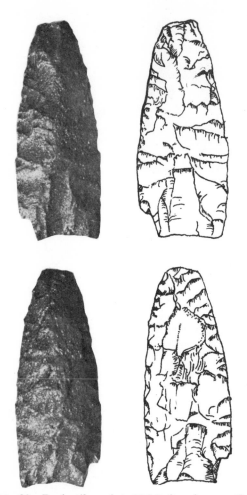

FIG. 20 Projectile point 64.9.2 found near the excavation. Natural size.

between 50 and 80 mm., seldom exceeding either extreme.

2. Plainview points are more neatly made than Clovis. The flaking is generally finer and more regular, displaying a greater degree of control. Well-controlled collateral flaking is to be found on many Plainview points.

3. Basal concavities on Plainview points are generally not as pronounced as those on Clovis points, but the variety within both types is such that this feature is not always distinctive. However, the transition from the basal concavity to the side of the point forms a rounded ear which is characteristic of both types.

4. Plainview points usually have marked parallel edges for part of their length whereas Clovis points have convex edges.

5. Clovis is, by definition, "fluted" where-

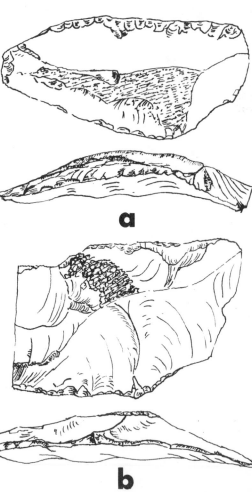

FIG. 21 Cutting tools from the Domebo locality. A—scraper on a blade, 64.9.1; B—worked flake, 64.9.4. Natural size.

Folsom and Eden typologies and placed considerable emphasis on Plainview as it pertained to that problem. In two subsequent publications (1947; 1949), Krieger stated that Plainview was intermediate between Clovis and the later Eden points, typologically as well as temporally. In general terms, Plainview points are often described as looking essentially like unfluted Clovis points (cf. Bell 1958: 74).

There is a considerable range of variation within both types, even in the collections from the type stations, but to date there has been no work on rigorously delimiting and describing the variations. Without going into a monographic treatment of the problems, a comparison of the two types may be summarized as follows:

1. Plainview points tend to be more uniform in size than Clovis. Clovis points may range from 25 to 150 mm., although 75 to 100 mm. seems the most usual length. Plainview points, on the other hand, range

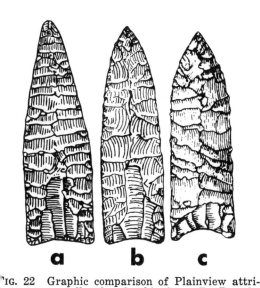

a   **b**   **c**

'IG. 22 Graphic comparison of Plainview attri-
utes, especially basal thinning. B—Domebo
pecimen 64.8.3; A and C—Plainview points from
he type site (reproduced from Sellards' *Early
Man in America* courtesy of the Texas Memorial
Museum and the University of Texas Press)

as Plainview is basally thinned by the removal of multiple long flakes.
6. Clovis points have always been found
associated with mammoth whereas Plainview points have always been found associated with extinct species of *Bison*.
7. Clovis is chronologically earlier than
Plainview.

Of these differences, only the last three
re individually significant, yet the presence or
bsence of a flute is the only truly diagnostic
eature. A flute, however, is still a badly defined
eature, even though various technological se-
uences for removing the channel flake have
een described (Roberts 1935; Witthoft 1952;
Mason 1958). On the basis of size, the distinc-
ion between a flute and a thinning flake is a
matter of degree, nor will technology alone dis-
inguish between the two, for many Plainview
oints exhibit techniques of removing thinning
lakes similar to the "Enterline" technique des-
ribed by Witthoft (1952). All of this under-
cores the essential fact that a "type" consists
f the conjunction of several attributes which
must be considered and weighed, each accord-
ng to its diagnostic importance.

The animal with which an artifact is found
must be dismissed as a typological criterion.
Thus far, where Clovis points have been found
n direct association with an animal, the animal
as been mammoth. Intriguing as this may be,
t does not demonstrate that the tool was made
xclusively for hunting large pachyderms, which,
f true, would be a cultural attribute of the type.
Moreover, mammoths killed by other than

Clovis-tipped projectiles have been found (Aveleyra-A. de Anda and Maldonado-Koerdell 1953;
Aveleyra-A. de Anda 1956) so the syllogism
"Clovis has always been found with mammoth,
ergo any point found with mammoth is Clovis"
is patently fallacious. The basic elements of
projectile point typology remain form and
technology.

The chronological difference between Clovis
and Plainview is real. Clovis finds, where ac-
ceptably dated, are currently limited to the time
span between 11,000 and 11,500 B.P. (Haynes
1964), while most available dates on Plainview
material cluster about 9,000 B.P. The nature of
most of the relevant samples, however, suggest
that 9,000 years B.P. is an upper limiting date.
Of the two dates on the Plainview bison bed,
Krieger (1957) considers one, 9,170±500, more
pertinent to the site. The other date of 7,100±
160 was from an apparently contaminated sample. Agogino (personal communication) reports
a date of 9,260 B.P. from a Plainview level near
Waco, Texas. A date of 9,524±450 from the
Lime Creek site in Nebraska is difficult to interpret since the sample came from well below the
Plainview horizon in that site. Davis (1962:31)
regards this date as "of uncertain reliability."
Bonfire Shelter near Langtry, Texas, produced
a date of 10,230±160 for a bone bed which contained bones of extinct bison, Plainview points
and a Folsom point (Pearson and others 1965).
This association indicates that Plainview may
be at least partially contemporary with the Folsom horizon which is dated between 10,000 and
11,000 B.P. by dates from five other sites (Haynes 1964). So, there is still a span of at least
1,000 years separating the Clovis and Plainview
types.

The two complete projectile points from
Domebo have been compared with a wide range
of both Clovis and Plainview points, including
specimens from each type site. The larger of
the two points is completely Clovis-like, but,
except for the flute, the smaller point might well
be called a Plainview. With respect to its size,
form and workmanship it is closely comparable
to most Plainview points, although the tendency
toward marked parallel edges is not greatly
pronounced. The multiple thinning flakes are
the most definite Plainview attribute. While
these are rather long, they only barely exceed
the range exhibited by the type specimens (Fig.
22). This style of basal thinning was not certainly identified on any Clovis point examined
in the course of the comparison. The reverse face
of this point is thinned by a flake which can
only be called a flute. The size, form and workmanship on the smaller Domebo point are individually comparable to occasional Clovis

23

FIG. 23 Tree stump No. 2 found downstream from bone bed dated 11,045 B.P. (SM-695). Boundary of Qdu and Qdl not conformable at this location and the top of the stump is covered by both blue clay and laminated brown sand.

points, but the quality of these attributes is, in general, more typical of Plainview.

The typological comparison is based on only two specimens. One point is completely Clovis-like; the other displays attributes of two different types, but the presence of a well defined flute is considered paramount in the assessment of typological criteria. Both points are assigned to the *Clovis* type, although reference of the smaller point to this type should be considered provisional. The perils of making such judgments from a single specimen considered, the Plainview-like characteristics of this point are regarded as significant, for they could represent a typological and technological, if not historical, transition between the more typical Clovis and Plainview forms. The medial fragment is too incomplete to permit typological placement but it probably represents a Clovis point. The typology of the fourth projectile point described is not considered in this discussion.

In sum: The projectile points from the Domebo excavations are classed as Clovis, but one of them displays attributes, particularly in form, workmanship and techniques of basal thinning which approach those generally associated with Plainview.

RADIOCARBON DATES

There are presently six radiocarbon dates pertaining to the Domebo site. Of these, three are on skeletal material, the other three date the lower member of the Domebo Formation.

The dates are presented and discussed in the order in which they were obtained.

1. TBN-311   4,952±304
                                      3,002 B. C.

Sample: Untreated tusk.

This date must be discarded as both too late and inconsistent. Vance Haynes (personal communication) informs us that bone, tusk and teeth are subject to contamination by humic acids and are generally unreliable for dating purposes without special pretreatment. The inconsistency is not fully explained, however, for subsequent dates show the humic acid contaminants in the bone to be as old as the bone itself. The source of contamination was most likely the humic slump deposits which overlay the skull but not the other bone. The tusk was also exposed to the stream for nearly a year.

2. SM-610   10,123±280
                                      8,173 B. C.

Sample: Lignitic wood.

The wood which provided the sample for this date was found by Bob H. Slaughter while washing matrix for micro-vertebrate fossils. The matrix was from within the excavation, about two feet higher than the level of the bone bed. The date may be considered the minimum terminal date for the lower member of the Domebo Formation.

3. SM-695   11,045±647
                                      9,095 B. C.

Sample: Wood.

The wood was from a buried stump identified by Forest Products Laboratory of Madison, Wisconsin, as belonging to the hard elm group and closely resembling the winged elm, *Ulmus alata*. It may be of interest to insert parenthetically that the specimen was notable for the slow growth exhibited: approximately fifty annual rings per inch of radius. The stump, one of three found near the excavation, was located approximately one hundred feet downstream from the bone bed. It was rooted in the marsh deposits at least thirty inches below the boundary of the upper and lower members of the Domebo Formation (Fig. 23). Because of the slope in the boundary, the base of the stump was actually about the same level as the bone bed. Beneath the stump was a lens of clay which probably marked the ground surface from which the tree grew. It could not be traced to the excavation, but there is the possibility that this ground surface would correlate with that on which the mammoth lay. On the basis of stratigraphic position this date was believed to be relevant to the deposition of the bone bed, a supposition supported by two subsequent dates on bone.

4. SI-172   11,220±500
       9,270 B. C.

Sample: Bone organics soluble in 2N HCl after initial 2% NaOH.

5. SI-175   11,200±600
       9,250 B. C.

Sample: Humic acids extracted after decalcification.

These two dates were obtained by Austin Long, Smithsonian Institution, on organic fractions separated from Domebo bone by Vance Haynes of the University of Arizona Geochronology Laboratories. The humic acids were removed from the sample and dated separately in an effort to determine the degree of contamination. As it turned out, the humic acids were as old as the bone, so the test was non-critical. The basic method of sample preparation used at Arizona has been described by Damon, Haynes and Long (1964: 91).

6. OX-56   9,400±300
       7,450 B. C.

Sample: Organic earth

The sample of organic earth for this date was collected by Anderson for Dr. Coyde Yost of the USDA Agricultural Research Service, Chickasha, Oklahoma. The sample was collected from near the skull, an area probably contaminated by the recent humic slump deposits which intruded the bone bed. Like TBN-311, from the same provenience, the date is inconsistent. Dr. L. L. McDowell of the USDA Agricultural Research Service, Oxford, Mississippi, who obtained the date, informs us (personal communication) that because of the small sample size no attempt was made to separate lignins and humic acids, and only inorganic carbonates were removed prior to processing the sample to benzene.

Excluding the dates on the tusk and soil, the radiocarbon dates on the Domebo mammoth and the lower member of the Domebo Formation constitute a consistent series. The Domebo dates are also consistent with other dated mammoth

kills. Including Domebo, there are now five radiocarbon-dated mammoth kill sites: the Lehner and Naco sites in Arizona, the Dent site in Colorado and the Blackwater Locality No.1 in New Mexico. The Lehner site is dated 11,260± 360 from an average of six dates (Damon, Haynes and Long 1964: 100); the Llano occupation at Blackwater Draw is dated 11,170±360 (Damon, Haynes and Long 1964: 101) and the Dent site is dated 11,200±500 (Haynes 1964: 1408). Two dates on the Naco site average 9,250±300 (Wise and Shutler 1958: 72), but this date has been questioned (Haury, Sayles and Wasley 1959: 25; Haynes 1964: 1410). The remarkable aspect of these dates is that, excepting the questionable Naco date, they are virtually identical.

Summary and Conclusions

About 11,200 years ago an Imperial Mammoth, *Mammuthus imperator*, was presumably killed and butchered in a canyon now known as Domebo Canyon. The bottom of the canyon was marshy, although it appears that the animal died on solid, if not dry, ground. The animal remains were soon covered by fine sand and then clay — a pond bottom — probably during a single flooding.

Three projectile points were found associated with the remains. Two are complete, one is fragmentary. The complete points are classed as *Clovis*, although one of them is aberrant. The Domebo site represents the easternmost association of this type of projectile point and an extinct animal found to date. In addition to the points, three small waste flakes were found in the bone bed; a fourth projectile point and two flake scrapers found downstream from the site may have been associated with the bone bed but displaced by erosion.

On the basis of projectile point type, megafauna and chronology, the Domebo site is assigned to the Llano Complex (Sellards 1952), thereby extending the known distribution of this complex to the eastern margin of the Great

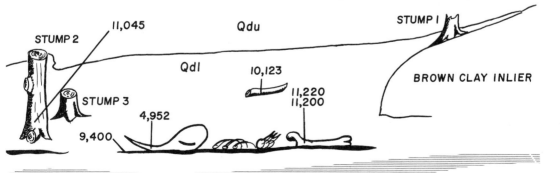

Fig. 24   Relationship of radiocarbon dates to geologic and archaeologic features.

Plains (cf. Haury, Sayles and Wasley 1959: 22-24; Wormington 1957: 43-84). Granted, the full range of artifacts known to comprise the Llano Complex was not found at Domebo, but the critical element, Clovis points in association with mammoth remains, was. The radiocarbon dates are consistent with dates from other mammoth kill sites, strengthening the contention that the hunters of the Domebo mammoth were culturally related to the people who hunted the mammoths found at Blackwater Draw, Naco, Lehner, Dent and other sites in the southern Plains and Southwest.

Λ

REFERENCES CITED

AVELEYRA-ARROYO DE ANDA, LUIS
1956 The Second Mammoth and Associated Artifacts at Santa Isabel, Iztapan, Mexico. *American Antiquity*, Vol. 22, No. 1. Salt Lake City.

AVELEYRA-ARROYO DE ANDA, LUIS, AND MANUAL MALDONADO-KOERDELL
1953 Association of Artifacts with Mammoth in the Valley of Mexico. *American Antiquiity*, Vol. 18, No. 4. Salt Lake City.

BELL, ROBERT E.
1958 A Guide to the Identification of Certain American Indian Projectile Points. *Special Bulletin of the Oklahoma Anthropological Society*, No. 1. Norman.

DAMON, PAUL E., C. VANCE HAYNES AND AUSTIN LONG
1964 Arizona Radiocarbon Dates V. *Radiocarbon*, Vol. 6. New Haven.

DAVIS, E. MOTT
1962 Archeology of the Lime Creek Site in Southwestern Nebraska. *Special Publication*, No. 3. University of Nebraska State Museum. Lincoln.

HAURY, EMIL W., E. B. SAYLES AND WILLIAM W. WASLEY
1959 The Lehner Mammoth Site, Southeastern Arizona. *American Antiquity*, Vol. 25, No. 1. Salt Lake City.

HAYNES, C. VANCE, JR.
1964 Fluted Projectile Points: Their Age and Dispersion. *Science*, Vol. 145, No. 3639. Washington, D. C.

KRIEGER, ALEX
1947 Certain Projectile Points of the Early American Hunters. *Bulletin of the Texas Archeological and Paleontological Society*, Vol. 18. Lubbock.

1949 The New Plainview Finds. *in* Proceedings of the Fifth Plains Conference of Archaeology, *Note Book* No. 1. Laboratory of Anthropology, University of Nebraska. Lincoln.

1957 Notes and News—Early Man. *American Antiquity*, Vol. 22, No. 3. Salt Lake City.

MASON, RONALD J.
1958 Late Pleistocene Geochronology and the Paleo-Indian Penetration into the Lower Michigan Peninsula. *Anthropological Papers*, No. 11. University of Michigan, Museum of Anthropology. Ann Arbor.

PEARSON, F. J., E. MOTT DAVIS, M. A. TAMERS AND ROBERT F. JOHNSTONE
1965 University of Texas Radiocarbon Dates III. *Radiocarbon*, Vol. 7. New Haven.

ROBERTS, FRANK H. H., JR.
1935 A Folsom Complex: Preliminary Report on Investigations at the Lindenmeier Site in Northern Colorado. Smithsonian Institution, *Miscellaneous Collections*, Vol. 94, No. 4. Washington, D. C.

SELLARDS, E. H.
1952 *Early Man in America*. Texas Memorial Museum and the University of Texas Press. Austin.

SELLARDS, E. H., G. L. EVANS AND G. E. MEADE
1947 Fossil Bison and Associated Artifacts from Plainview, Texas (with description of artifacts by Alex D. Krieger). *Bulletin of the Geological Society of Amercia*, Vol. 58, No. 10. Baltimore.

WISE, E. N. AND DICK SHUTLER, JR.
1958 University of Arizona Radiocarbon Dates. *Science*, Vol. 127, No. 3289. Washington.

WITTHOFT, JOHN
1952 A Paleo-Indian Site in Eastern Pennsylvania: An Early Hunting Culture. *Proceedings of the American Philosophical Society*, Vol. 96, No. 4. Philadelphia.

WORMINGTON, H. M.
1957 *Ancient Man in North America*. Denver Museum of Natural History. Denver.

THE DOMEBO MAMMOTH: VERTEBRATE PALEOMORTOLOGY

M. G. Mehl

When invited by Mr. Marvin E. Tong, Jr., Director of the Museum of the Great Plains, to participate in the excavation of the Domebo site, I found it possible to spend something more than two weeks at the project during the initial stages of bone excavation early in March of 1962. At that time I assisted Mr. Adrian Anderson with the anatomical identification of bones as they were exposed and helped with the problems of their excavation, packaging and removal from the narrow, steep-sided valley where they occurred. In the later part of May of the same year I participated in the conference at the Museum of the Great Plains with the several specialists who had been assisting in the solution of problems presented by the dig. I also had the opportunity to examine some of the major skeletal elements that had been removed from crates and protective bandages. The discussion of paleomortology [1] presented in the paragraphs that follow is based on this limited field experience, the later conference and the limited laboratory examination of some of the better preserved bones. I also have before me the excavation plot made by Mr. Anderson and his assistant, Mr. Lee McNair.

Detailed descriptions of individual bones of the Domebo mammoth are of little interest at this stage and are obviously impossible at this time. Instead, I have resorted to outlines of key pieces, such as propodials and epipodials, as they have been photographed through a screen of one-inch mesh. Aside from the identification of the animal, the major effort in this report has been toward the adequate representation of the distribution of the bones and the most likely explanation for the peculiar dispersal pattern.

[1]Mehl describes *Vertebrate Paleomortology* as an attempt "to accumulate and interpret all the data bearing on the death and postmortem events of each skeletal find that offers some chance of demonstrating 'man-animal' association."—Ed.

IDENTIFICATION

The large skeletal elements exposed in the Domebo dig unquestionably represent a species of the genus *Mammuthus,* and I refer them to *M. imperator* with some confidence. This form, as the vertebrate paleontologist conventionally delineates species, is remarkably variable with age and sex, particularly in body size and tusk development. The typical molar pattern is indicated in the diagram of the much abraded left lower second molar (Fig. 25). The unerupted left lower molar number 3 consists of nineteen ridge plates as indicated in Figure 26. The first eight of these show the thick coating and separation by cement that is typical of the species.

I find no clue to the sex other than the comparatively small tusks. Only the left tusk was sufficiently preserved to indicate its characteristics. It is small, about seven inches in diameter at the butt, and probably not more than four feet long. It has a strong upward curve and a dextral twist. It is likely that "Domebo" was a female regardless of the fact that the estimated height at the shoulder is between thirteen and fourteen feet. Although the animal is immature, as evidenced by the unfused epiphyses of most of the long bones, all four of the second molars were reaching the end of their triturational service. This immaturity of the skeleton included the ready separation of the pelvis from the sacrum and the separation of the two halves of the pelvis from each other.

MAJOR SALVAGABLE PARTS

SKULL: Badly disintegrated by comparatively recent erosion with only a part of the left tusk alveolus readily recognizable; left tusk shattered and a foot or more of the tip missing; right tusk shattered and dispersed; right and left upper molars No. 2 intact; left lower molar No. 3 well preserved; numerous separate and some-

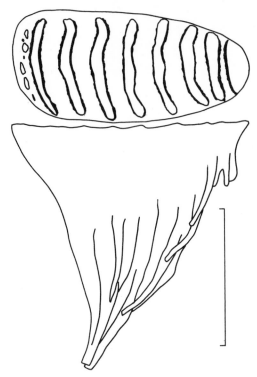

FIG. 25 Superior and lateral views of lower left second molar. Line=10 cm.

what scattered ridge plates presumably representing both upper and lower third molars well preserved.

LIMBS: Both humeri, both femora, both ulnae and the right tibia are recognizable (Fig. 27); incomplete shafts presumably represent radii and fibulae; somewhat scattered mesopodials, metapodials and phalanges probably represent the right forefoot.

VERTEBRAE: A few cervical, anterio-dorsal, perhaps lumbar, and the sacrum, all poorly preserved and currently concealed by bandages.

SCAPULAE: Left fairly well preserved; right broken into large and small pieces by comparatively recent erosion and scattered by the closely adjacent stream.

PELVIC GIRDLE: Left half intact; right half broken and dissipated; a large piece of the ilium, including the acetabular surface, recovered about thirty feet downstream.

RIBS: A dozen or less, fairly well preserved and not widely scattered.

MAJOR MISSING ELEMENTS

The partial or complete loss of major skeletal elements such as the right tibia and the right innominate of the pelvis and the right scapula seems best explained by the assumption that they were probably dragged by predators into the area that in comparatively recent times

became part of the recent actively eroded area bordering the east side of the excavation. Smaller and lighter units such as vertebrae, ribs, mesopodials, metapodials and phalanges (conventionally minimized except where a swamp or sinkhole trap has been involved) seem, most likely, to have been dragged beyond the area of excavation by smaller of the vertebrate scavengers. I find no ready explanation for the fact that most of the bones of the foot remained in proximity to one front leg in the present case.

DISPERSAL PATTERN OF REMAINS

The accompanying bone dispersal plat (Fig. 28) is not intended to replace the one by Anderson, but to help visualize the transportation mechanics involved. It omits all the lesser elements such as might be shifted readily or carried away by smaller predators and scavengers. The heavy sigmoidal curve does not represent an unbroken series of vertebrae, but rather the probable trend of the column immediately following death of the mammoth. This is based on the assumption that the skull was not markedly shifted before burial. The position of the isolated sacrum and the occipital region of the skull at the time the bones were exposed during excavation determined this choice. Except for the pelvis and hind leg, the shifting of large bones is not great and is about as would be expected of large predatory carnivores. However, the possibility of intervention by contemporary man cannot be arbitrarily dismissed.

THE DEATH FLOOR

The surface on which the animal died was essentially level and without perceptible relief. The carcass rested on its left side with feet extended in the direction of subsequent major dispersal. There is nothing in the sediments to indicate a hostile environment. The apparently undisturbed surface of the floor is good evidence that the animal was not "sediment trapped."

INTERVAL BETWEEN DEATH AND BURIAL

None of the bone is well preserved, excepting pieces that have been secondarily exposed intermittently within the active erosion area to the east of the scapula. Several of these pieces are somewhat mineralized and hard. The spongy nature of other elements may be due in part to

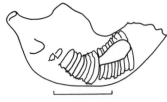

FIG. 26 Inner lateral view of left ramus showing nineteen ridge plates of unerupted third molar in approximately life position. Line=20 cm.

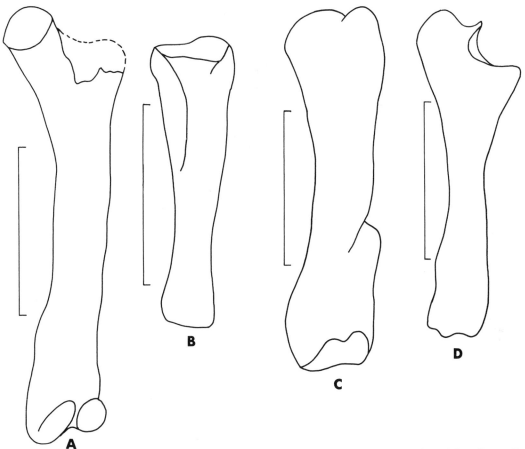

FIG. 27 Propodials and epipodials of Domebo mammoth. A—right femur; B—right tibia; C—left humerus; D—left ulna. Lines=50 cm.

pre-burial exposure. It is more likely, however, that this poor preservation is largely the result of subsurface weathering. The zone of bone accumulation and stratum immediately above are markedly water permeable. That there was some delay in burial is evidenced by unmistakable grooves made by rodent teeth on the free edge of the acromion ridge and on a large fragment of the right scapula.

MAN-ANIMAL ASSOCIATION

According to the records of Mr. Anderson and Mr. Leonhardy two projectile points and some flakes were found on the actual "death floor" within the area of bone distribution. Their proximity to any particular bone in the dispersal pattern does not seem significant. Other artifacts found along the stream that cuts the floor are, almost certainly, time records of equal importance but can scarcely be included in the death story or subsequent events involving this animal. There is no suggestion of "stacking," the abnormal association of skeletal parts that would require tossing or actual carrying of bones from one place to another. On the other hand, stacking could have been part of the original picture, details of which were erased by subsequent dragging. The same can be said if an explanation for the absence of hack marks on any of the bones that have been closely examined seems to be required. It is not likely that such marks would be retained by the poorly preserved surfaces. The absence of green bone fracture and possible percussion instruments at the Domebo dig may have no particular significance, but it is very disappointing in the light of the remarkable "bone cracking record" so well preserved in the Cooperton dig of a year earlier, at a distance of only about thirty miles. [2]

PALEOPATHOLOGY

There is some evidence that the Domebo elephant had a penchant for quarreling with others of its kind. The acromion ridge of the right scapula was split at mid-width for more than half its length and laterally telescoped. Although the preservation of the bone is such

[2]*See* Anderson, Adrian D., 1962: The Cooperton Mammoth: A Preliminary Report. *Plains Anthropologist*, Vol. 7, No. 16, pp. 110-112. Lincoln.—Ed.

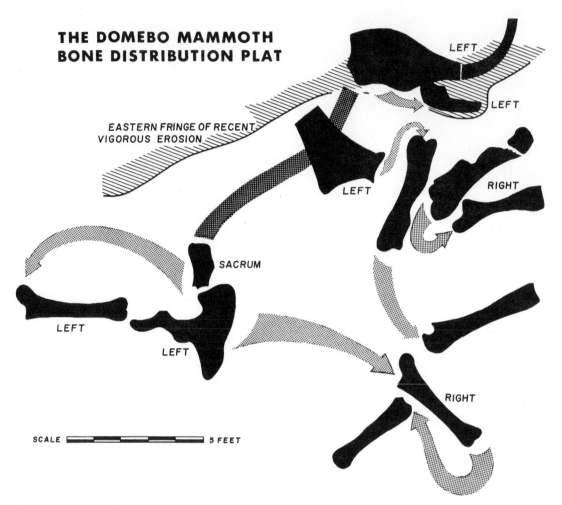

THE DOMEBO MAMMOTH BONE DISTRIBUTION PLAT

EASTERN FRINGE OF RECENT VIGOROUS EROSION

LEFT

LEFT

LEFT

RIGHT

SACRUM

LEFT

LEFT

RIGHT

SCALE 5 FEET

FIG. 28 Burial position of major appendicular units (scapula, propodials, pelvis and epipodials). Arrows indicate relation of the several parts to each other and the direction of their displacement. The sinuous, cross-hachured band connecting the skull and the sacrum indicates the supposed position of the vertebral column at the time of the animal's death. Reference to Figure 27 will identify most of the appendicular pieces.

that one cannot be sure whether there was some regrowth, the two halves cannot be separated and restored to normal relationship without first breaking the bone. The skeleton of a mastodon, assembled at the University of Wisconsin about fifty year ago records an encounter with an adversary that resulted in several broken ribs, subsequently repaired by nature leaving only the unmistakable scars. I do not know of another proboscidian scapula having been injured in the manner suggested, but I believe the explanation may have merit.

CAUSE OF DEATH

Although it is perhaps the trend of the times to assume that the two projectile points found intimately associated with the bones of the Domebo mammoth were at least contributory

to the animal's death, I do not believe that this assumption is justified. While the "contemporaneity of man and mammoth" for the Domebo situation seems well established, the assumption of human kill and/or butcher departs from the scientific exactitude we have come to expect of the archaeologist.

I believe that one is justified in assuming that there is a causal relationship between the Domebo mammoth and the projectile points found in the same limited area and on the same "death floor." It seems likely that the projectile points were carried in the flesh of the elephant, but it is possible that they were aimed at scavengers or predators gathered at this spot. It is also possible that the points actually caused the death of the elephant. It seems best to record "Cause of Death Unknown."

THE VERTEBRATES OF THE DOMEBO LOCAL FAUNA, PLEISTOCENE OF OKLAHOMA

Bob H. Slaughter

EXCLUSIVE OF THE MAMMOTH MATERIAL which led to the discovery of the Domebo Site, the specimen of *Geochelone* found by Anderson while excavating the elephant and the maxillary fragment of fossil bison, the vertebrate material discussed here was recovered from approximately three thousand pounds of matrix removed from two localities within two hundred yards of each other. Less than one-fifth of the matrix was taken from the actual elephant quarry and this produced but two identifiable specimens, the cotton rat and the pocket mouse. There is no doubt, however, that the other material is contemporary since the blue-black silt of the lower member of the Domebo Formation may be traced downstream the two hundred yards to the waterfall, site of the second quarry. The quarried matrix was taken to Southern Methodist University where is was dried and washed using the technique outlined by Hibbard (1949).

FAUNAL LIST

Class AMPHIBIA
  Order SALIENTIA
    Family HYLIDAE
      Acris crepitans Baird
    Family RANIDAE
      Rana pipiens Schreber
Class REPTILIA
  Order SQUAMATA
    Family COLUBRIDAE
      Thamnophis sauritus (Linnaeus)
    Family CROTALIDAE
      Genus and species indent
  Order CHELONIA[1]
    Family TESTUDINIDAE
      Geochelone cf. *G. wilsoni* (Milstead)

[1]Most of the carapace, plastron and internal skeletal elements of a turtle were found in the lower member of the Domebo Formation by Leonhardy in October, 1965. This material is provisionally identified by Slaughter as *Terrapene carolina putnami*.

Class MAMMALIA
  Order RODENTIA
    Family HETEROMYIDAE
      Perognathus hispidus Baird
    Family GEOMYIDAE
      Geomys cf. *G. bursarius* (Shaw)
    Family CRICETIDAE
      Sigmodon hispidus Say and Ord
      Microtus ochrogaster (Wagner)
            or
        M. pinetorum (Le Conte)
      Ondatra zibethicus (Linnaeus)
      Synaptomys cf. *S. cooperi* Baird
  Order ARTIODACTYLA
    Family BOVIDAE
      Bison antiquus (Leidy)
            or
      B. occidentalis Lucas

NOTES ON FAUNA

Class AMPHIBIA

Acris crepitans Baird
Cricket Frog
Referred specimens — Two left ilia, MGP catalog 64.8.7.
Discussion — This little cricket frog inhabits low vegetation along the moist banks of small streams as well as the shallows of larger bodies of water. Live specimens were collected within a few feet of the fossil producing site.

Rana pipiens Schreber
Leopard Frog
Referred specimens — Two left ilia, MPG catalog 64.8.8.
Discussion — Leopard frogs may be found near almost any body of water, large or small, and were collected alive in the stream that has exposed the Pleistocene deposits at the Domebo site.

Class REPTILIA

Thamnophis sauritus (Linnaeus)
Ribbon Snake

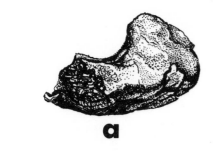

a

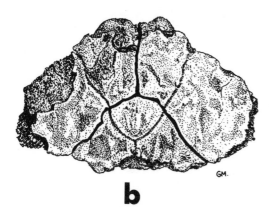

b

FIG. 29 *Geochelone* cf. *G. wilsoni* (Milstead), anterior fragment of plastron. A—lateral view; B—ventral view. Natural size.

Referred specimen — Vertebra, MGP catalog 64.8.9.

Discussion — The ribbon snake still lives in most marshes and sloughs of Oklahoma, but it is rarely found far from water.

CROTALIDAE — genus indent.
Pit Viper

Referred specimen — Vertebra, MGP catalong 64.8.10.

Discussion — Dr. Holman states that the single vertebra of an intermediate-sized pit viper represents an immature individual and is not identifiable. The rattlesnake, *Crotalus*, and the copperhead, *Ancistrodon*, occur in the area today.

Geochelone cf. *G. wilsoni* (Milstead)
Extinct Tortoise
(Fig. 29)

Referred specimen — Anterior fragment of plastron containing complete right and left epiplastron and anterior one-half of the entoplastron, MGP catalog 64.8.22.

Description and discussion — The beak of the epiplastron projects from the margin of the plastron moderately abruptly and is plainly notched. The maximum thickness of the beak is 21.4 millimeters and the preserved thickness of the entoplastron is 11.7 millimeters. The transverse diameter at the posterior edges of the epiplastral elements is 63.3 millimeters.

The specimen was compared with the holo-type of *Geochelone wilsoni* and the associated specimens from Friesenhahn Cave, Baxter County, Texas. Only one important difference was noted: the thickness of the plastron at the entoplastron is somewhat greater than the like-sized specimens from the type locality. However, considering the similarities and the age of the material from Texas and Oklahoma, the specimen is provisionally referred to that species. The Domebo specimen was shown to Dr. Walter Affenburg who compared its measurements with a series taken from the Friesenhahn material, and he agreed that it probably does represent an individual of Wilson's tortoise.

The Domebo site is not only the most northern reported occurrence of this tortoise, but the radiocarbon date of approximately 10,000 BP furnishes a minimum terminal date for the extinct species. Living members of the genus *Geochelone* are restrcted to tropical and subtropical habitats.

Class MAMMALIA
Perognathus hispidus Baird
Pocket Mouse

Referred specimen — Left p4, MGP catalog 64.8.13.

Discussion — The hispid pocket mouse still lives in the Domebo area, inhabiting sandy fields sparsely covered with vegetation.

Geomys cf. *G. bursarius* (Shaw)
Gopher

Referred specimens — Two fragmentary incisors, MGP catalog 64.8.12.

Discussion — Although incisors are not specifically diagnostic, it is probable that this widely distributed species is represented. Live specimens were collected within one hundred yards of the Domebo Site.

Sigmodon hispidus Say and Ord
Cotton Rat

Referred specimens — Right lower jaw containing m3, MGP catalog 64.8.14; M1, MGP catalog 64.8.19.

Discussion — The hispid cotton rat's current range includes all of Oklahoma, but the apparent absence of this species in Wisconsin deposits in Northern Oklahoma may indicate that the whole of this state is a relatively recent range acquisition; the oldest specimens from this general area are of Sangamon age (Slaughter *et al*, 1962; Slaughter and Ritchie 1963).[2] The habitat of the cotton rat is fields, with or with-

[2]Slaughter (1966, *Journal of Paleontology*, Vol. 40, No. 1) has shown the difficulties of assigning southern fossil faunas stage names based upon evidence of glacial advance and retreat in the north and preferred simply to consider the Easley Ranch, Moore Pit and Clear Creek local faunas merely as belonging to the interstadial or interglacial period which ended about 25,000 B. P. The reader may place that event where he chooses.

out trees, but with rather dense stands of high grass.

Microtus ochrogaster (Wagner)
or
M. pinetorum (Le Conte)
Vole

Referred specimens — Two right lower jaws containing m1 and m2, MGP catalog 64.8.15 and 64.8.16.

Discussion — The pine vole and the prairie vole cannot be separated with the material at hand. Both live in the general area of the Domebo site today, but they have very different habitats. The prairie vole lives on tall grass prairies and is often found associated with Domebo faunal member, *Sigmodon*. The pine vole, on the other hand, prefers wooded areas where it builds shallow runways in the sand and surface runways under leaves. Both habitats are available in the immediate area and it may well be that both species are represented in the fossil fauna.

Ondatra zibethicus (Linnaeus)
Muskrat

Referred specimen — Left m2, MGP catalog 64.8.17.

Discussion — If the muskrat is not in the vicinity today, it is due to the activities of man in recent years. The presence of muskrat certainly is indicative of more-or-less permanent ground water and lends support to the suggestion of the presence of a marsh as indicated by the molluscan fauna.

Synaptomys cf. S. cooperi Baird
Bog Lemming

Referred specimen — Left m2, MGP catalog 64.8.18.

Discussion — Because the cheek teeth of lemmings are evergrowing and because the extinct species *S. australus* can only be distinguished from *S. cooperi* by the former's greater size, positive identification of teeth within the size range of the living species cannot be made. *S. australus* has been reported from north central Texas by Dalquest (1962) and from northeastern Texas by Slaughter and Ritchie (1963) but both of these occurrences are considered Sangamon. *S. australus* has not been recognized in deposits as young as those at Domebo.

Bison antiquus (Leidy)
or
B. occidentalis Lucas
Extinct Bison

Referred specimen — Fragment of right maxillary containing P4-M3, MGP catalog 64.8.29.

Discussion — This specimen was collected

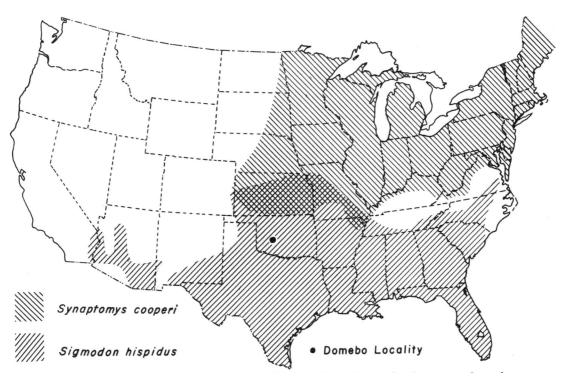

Fig. 30 Current ranges of two members of the Domebo local fauna showing area of overlap.

Synaptomys cooperi

Sigmodon hispidus

● Domebo Locality

TABLE 1
Comparison of measurements of *Bison*, MGP 64.8.29

	MGP 64.8.29	*Bison bison* (after Skinner & Kaisen, 1947)			*Bison occidentalis* (After Skinner & Kaisen, 1947)			*Bison antiquus* (after Chandler, 1916)		
								UC21185	UC21143	UC21184
	mm.	Min. mm.	Ave. mm.	Max.	Min. mm.	Ave. mm.	Max.		mm.	
Anteroposterior diameter of P4	21.5	—	—	—	—	—	—	19	21	19
Transverse diameter of P4	24.3	—	—	—	—	—	—	26	28	25
Anteroposterior diameter of M1	28.2	—	—	—	—	—	—	30	29	28
Transverse diameter of M1	27.4*	—	—	—	—	—	—	31	30	28
Anteroposterior diameter of M2	35.5	—	—	—	—	—	—	34.5	37	34
Transverse diameter of M2	29.4	—	—	—	—	—	—	33.5	31	30
Anteroposterior diameter of M3	36.4	—	—	—	—	—	—	36	39	36
Transverse diameter of M3	31.9	—	—	—	—	—	—	32	29	33
P2-M3 length	164.6	129	147	157	137	147	160			
M1-M3 length	99.0	82	91	98	84	91	102			

* approximate

by Mr. Lee Adams from the very top of the black silt at the waterfall quarry.

Tooth characters are not specifically diagnostic in *Bison*, but the measurements of this specimen are definitely beyond the size range of the living species, *Bison bison*. There are two extinct species, *B. antiquus* and *B. occidentalis*, with which the size of the Domebo bison agrees (Table 1). Both have been recovered elsewhere from deposits of the same approximate age and in association with Early Man.

CONCLUSIONS

If the bog lemming represented in the Domebo collection is *Synaptomys cooperi* rather than a young individual of *S. australus*, it is the only extant species that does not live in the area today. The current southern limits of this species' range is over two hundreds miles to the north. This would indicate that during the deposition of the Domebo sediments, summers may have lacked the high temperatures that occur in southern Oklahoma today. On the other hand, the presence of the typically tropical genus *Geochelone* suggests that winters probably were not as severe, and certainly lacked prolonged freezing tempera-

tures. This further substantiates the conclusions of Slaughter and Hoover (1963) as to the climate of northeast Texas between 11,000 and 9,500 B.P. based on mammals of the Ben Franklin local fauna in Delta County, Texas. Here a more equate, but cooler, climate was suggested by the sympatry of such southern types as the cotton rat and armadillo with such typically northern forms as the masked shrew, the meadow vole and the southern bog lemming. The ranges of the bog lemming and the cotton rat overlap today in Kansas, although both were present in southern Oklahoma during Domebo deposition (Fig. 30).

As the number of well-dated Pleistocene faunas grows, it becomes increasingly evident that none could be construed to suggest a climate with winters more severe than we endure today. A close examination of these faunas seems to indicate that in "pre-modern" climate, at least during the Late Pleistocene, winters were warmer while summers were either cooler or about the same during interglacials and interstadials; during the glacial stages summers were somewhat cooler while winters were no more severe than today, and in fact were probably less so.

SUMMARY

The vertebrates of the Domebo local fauna suggest that deposition was made in a shallow marsh or slough which was surrounded by low, moist vegetation. In the immediate valley there were woods and areas of tall grass. Tall grass may have also been present on the upland prairie, but there were at least some places nearby where the ground was sparsely covered with vegetation. Prolonged cold winter temperatures probably did not occur, and the summers were at least slightly cooler. Rainfall may not have differed significantly from that of today. The ratio of complete jaws to fragmentary specimens indicates that the fossils had not washed far. The upland varieties such as gopher and pocket mouse could have been brought to the marsh by owls.

ACKNOWLEDGEMENTS

I should like to express my appreciation to Frank Schneider who aided greatly in the collecting; to Marvin E. Tong, Jr., and Adrian Anderson, Museum of the Great Plains, for locating fossiliferous zones, acquiring financial aid, and offering helpful suggestions. I am also grateful to Dr. J. Alan Holman, Illinois State Normal University, for furnishing the frog and snake identifications.

REFERENCES CITED

CHANDLER, ASA C.
1916 A Study of the Skull and Dentition of *Bison antiquus* Leidy, with Special Reference to Material from the Pacific Coast. *University of California Publications, Department of Geology*, Vol. 9, No. 11. Berkeley.

DALQUEST, WALTER W.
1962 The Good Creek Formation, Pleistocene of Texas, and its Fauna. *Journal of Paleontology*, Vol. 36. Tulsa.

HIBBARD, CLAUDE W.
1949 Techniques of Collecting Microvertebrate Fossils. *Contributions of the Museum of Paleontology, University of Michigan*, Vol. 16. Ann Arbor.

SKINNER, MORRIS F. AND OVE C. KAISEN
1947 The Fossil Bison of Alaska and a Preliminary Revision of the Genus. *Bulletin of the American Museum of Natural History*, Vol. 89. New York.

SLAUGHTER, BOB H., ET AL
1962 The Hill-Shuler Local Faunas of the Upper Trinity River in Dallas and Denton Counties, Texas. *University of Texas, Bureau of Economic Geology, Report of Investigations*, No. 48. Austin.

SLAUGHTER, BOB H. AND B. REED HOOVER
1963 Sulphur River Formation and the Pleistocene Mammals of the Ben Franklin Local Fauna. *Journal of the Graduate Research Center*, Vol. 31, No. 3. Dallas.

SLAUGHTER, BOB H. AND RONALD RITCHIE
1963 Pleistocene Mammals of the Clear Creek Local Fauna, Denton County, Texas. *Journal of the Graduate Research Center*, Vol. 31, No. 3. Dallas.

ECOLOGICAL SIGNIFICANCE OF THE FOSSIL FRESH-WATER AND LAND SHELLS FROM THE DOMEBO MAMMOTH KILL SITE

E. P. Cheatum and Don Allen

IN MARCH, 1962, the senior author was extended an invitation by Mr. Marvin E. Tong, Jr., Director of the Museum of the Great Plains, Lawton, Oklahoma, to visit the excavation of the mammoth kill near Stecker, Oklahoma, to collect invertebrate fossils and to make paleo-ecological interpretations from them. In April, 1962, a trip was made to the site and with the assistance of Mr. Adrian Anderson, director of the excavation, samples were collected for study. Subsequently, Anderson sent matrix from strategic locations within the excavation for analysis.

Since this study is concerned almost exclusively with the fossil mollusks from the excavation, a brief resume of the more significant contributions on Oklahoma mollusks, both recent and fossil, seems appropriate. Branson, in a series of three publications (1959, 1961a, 1961b), has provided the most comprehensive information on the distribution, taxonomy and ecology of the fresh-water and land gastropods of Oklahoma. Prior to this work, Simpson (1888), Pilsbry (1899, 1902, 1903), Ferriss (1900, 1906), Pilsbry and Ferriss (1902), Walker (1909, 1915), Baker (1909) and Greger (1915) contributed to the knowledge of the Oklahoma recent gastropod fauna. Publications of Leonard and Franzen (1944, 1946) and Franzen and Leonard (1947) have added to the knowledge of both recent and fossil Oklahoma gastropods and have provided an insight on the origin of the Oklahoma fauna.

Among the species of fossil shells listed in this study are *Lymnaea caperata*, *Promenetus umbilicatellus* (with the exception of an isolated occurrence in northeastern Oklahoma. [Taylor, 1960]), *Succinea ovalis*, *Cionella lubrica*, *Retinella roemeri*, *Discus cronkhitei*, *Sphaerium occidentale* and *Pisidium variable* which, according to known records, are not recent for Oklahoma. Leonard and Franzen (1944) in their study of the Laverne formation (Pliocene) in

Beaver county, Oklahoma, listed only two species of gastropods, *Hawaiia minuscula* and *Vertigo ovata*, which were collected from the mammoth site. Dr. Claude Hibbard, University of Michigan Museums (personal correspondence, September 19, 1962), informs us that *Valvata tricarinata* and *Vertigo ovata*, which are present in the Domebo collection, are also in the Laverne collection at the University of Michigan.

Among the Pleistocene gastropods of Oklahoma which were found at Domebo are the following species (with references): Frye and Leonard (1952), Pearlette Ash faunas, Beaver, Woodword and Washita Counties, *V. tricarinata*, *Lymnaea caperata*, *Physa anatina*, *Physa gyrina*, *Gastrocopta armifera*, *Gastrocopta contracta*, *V. ovata*, *Helicodiscus parallelus*, *H. minuscula*, *Retinella electrina*, *C. lubrica* and *S. ovalis* (Taylor [1960] includes the Pearlette Ash faunas under the term Cudahy which was used by Hibbard [1949b] to designate a broader glacial fauna of Kansan age); Hibbard and Taylor (1960), Berends local fauna in Beaver County, *L. caperata*, *P. gyrina*, *P. anatina*, *G. armifera*, *G. contracta*, *V. ovata*, *H. parallelus*, *Helicodiscus singleyanus*, *D. cronkhitei*, *R. electrina*, *H. minuscula*, *Euconulus fulvus*, *C. lubrica*, *Vallonia gracilicosta*, *Fossaria parva* (*Lymnaea dalli?*), and *Stenotrema leai*.

PROCEDURE

Matrix sent for examination came from seven specific localities in or near the evcavated area. From these seven localities, the three which contained the greatest concentration of shells were selected for study. Anderson, in correspondence (August 20, 1962) pertaining to the homogeneity of shell distribution in the matrix, states: "shells appear to occur with greater frequency in the clayey-silt than in the sand, due, I suspect, to the sand lenses having been formed during periods of excessive run-

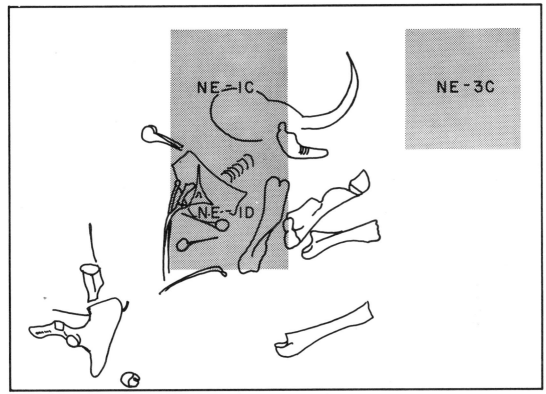

FIG. 31   Proveniences of mollusks in the Domebo excavation.

off, washing the shells downstream." He also describes the matrix containing the shells as "alternating layers of blue clayey-silt and grey sands. These layers, or bands, intermesh, feather out into one another, etc., so that there are only general areas which can be said to be even *relatively* continuous across the excavated area." Matrix samples designated "Below the Waterfall" were collected by Mr. Bob H. Slaughter of Southern Methodist University from an area approximately 200 yards downstream from the mammoth kill site.

The samples of matrix sent us by Anderson were designated as NE-3D, NE-1C and NE-1D (Fig. 31). An interpretation of the code name of each of these locations is as follows: the excavation was laid out in four quadrants, of which only two, the northeast and southeast, were used. Each quadrant was divided into five-foot squares labelled A, B, C, etc., from the center toward the east; and 1, 2, 3, etc., from the center toward the north and south. Thus, the designation NE-3D, for instance, refers to the third square in the D line of the northeast quadrant. Sample NE-1C was from a black silt immediately west of the skull at bone level; sample NE-3D was from a blue clay zone; and sample NE-1D was from grey sand beneath the scapula.

The samples of matrix were processed by the technique described by Hibbard (1949). Eight species of fresh-water gastropods, twenty-one species of land gastropods and two species of sphaerids were recovered. Five families of fresh-water gastropods and ten families of land gastropods are represented in the collection.

Also recovered were three species of ostracod shells which were sent to Dr. E. D. Gutentag, State Geological Survey of Kansas, for identification. Dr. Gutentag identified these shells as follows: "*Cypridopsis vidua* (O. F. Muller, 1776) adult and immature instars, Pliocene to Recent; *Candona crogmaniana* (Turner, 1894) adult complete carapace and fragments of female carapaces, Late Pliocene to Recent; *Candona* cf. *C. renoensis* (Gutentag and Benson, 1962), Upper Pliocene to Late Pleistocene?" Dr. Gutentag also stated that "these same forms are present in the Pleistocene beds of southwestern Kansas."

LIST OF MOLLUSKS COLLECTED WITH DISTRIBUTIONAL AND ECOLOGICAL NOTES

FRESH-WATER PELECYPODS

Family SPHAERIDAE
Sphaerium occidentale Prime
  Distribution—New Brunswick, Quebec, Ontario; Vermont, Massachusetts, Connecticut,

New York, New Jersey, Pennsylvania, Delaware, Virginia, South Carolina, Tennessee, Alabama, Georgia, Ohio, Michigan, Indiana, Wisconsin, Illinois, Montana, Wyoming, Washington, Oregon, ldaho, Utah and Colorado (Herrington 1962).

Habitat—"Still waters of swamps, ditches and ponds; among grass and leaves. This species has a preference for, or requires, a habitat that dries up for part of the year" (Herrington 1962).

Remarks—"Fossil specimens of *S. occidentale* have been identified in Late Pleistocene deposits of Sangamon Age (Jinglebob fauna) in Meade County Kansas" (Herrington 1962).

Pisidium variable Prime

Distribution—Prince Edward Island, New Brunswick, Quebec, Ontario, Saskatchewan and British Columbia; Maine, Vermont, Massachusetts, Rhode Island, Connecticut, New York, New Jersey, Pennsylvania, District of Columbia, Tennessee, Alabama, Ohio, Michigan, Indiana, Wisconsin, Illinois, South Dakota, Iowa, Montana, Washington, Idaho, California, Utah, and Colorado (Herrington 1962).

Habitat—"Creeks, rivers and lakes; usually in still water where soft sediments accumulate" (Herrington 1962).

FRESH-WATER GASTROPODS

Family VALVATIDAE

Valvata tricarinata (Say)

Distribution—"Eastern United States west to Iowa; Great Slave Lake south to Virginia and the Ohio River" (Baker 1928).

Habitat—Requires permanent water; occurs in rivers and lakes.

Family AMNICOLIDAE

Pomatiopsis lapidaria (Say)

Distribution—"New York to (Northeastern Kansas) Iowa, Michigan, Wisconsin, south to Missouri, Alabama, and Georgia" (Baker 1928).

Habitat—Amphibious; often found on damp ground and on other moist surfaces, sometimes many yards from water.

Family PHYSIDAE

Physa anatina Lea

Distribution—"Probably the species occurs in most of the central and southern Great Plains" (Hibbard and Taylor 1960). This species is today the most abundant of the Physidae in Texas.

Habitat—Usually found in quiet waters, but also occurs in moderate stream currents; associated with algae.

Physa gyrina (Say)

Distribution—Recorded from the Arctic Regions south to Alabama and Texas (Baker 1928). Its southern range needs considerable

clarification since we have not recognized this species in any of our collections of recent physids from Texas.

Habitat—Thrives best in quiet waters and slow-moving streams where algae grow in abundance.

Family LYMNAEIDAE

Lymnaea caperata (Say)

Distribution—"From Quebec and Massachusetts west to California; Yukon Territory and James Bay south to Maryland, Indiana, Colorado, and California" (Baker 1928).

Habitat—"This species seems to almost invariably occupy intermittent streams or small pools, ponds and ditches which dry up in the summer" (Baker 1928).

Lymnaea dalli (Baker)

Distribution—"Ohio to Northern Michigan and Montana, south to Kansas and Arizona" (Baker 1928).

Habitat—Baker (1928) states that it "Inhabits wet, marshy places, generally out of the water, on sticks, stones, or muddy flats."

Remarks—Branson (1961) following Hubendick (1951) synonymized *L. parva* Lea, *L. dalli* (Baker), *L. obrussa*, and *L. modicella* (Say) under *Lymnaea humilis* Say. Our specimens conform to those identified by van der Schalie (correspondence, June 1962) as *L. dalli*.

Family PLANORBIDAE

Gyraulus parvus (Say)

Distribution—"North America, from Alaska and Northern Canada to Cuba and from the Atlantic to the Pacific coast. Perhaps also in Northern Eurasia" (Taylor 1960).

Habitat—"Usually in quiet bodies of water, often of small size—*parvus* is partial to a habitat which has rather thick vegetation. This species is more often found in vegetation than in any other situation" (Baker 1928).

Promenetus umbilicatellus (Cockerell).

Distribution—"North America north of about lat. 41° from Nevada and Alaska east and southeast to western New York; south in the Rocky Mountains to southern Colorado; an isolated occurrence in the Ozark Mountains, northeastern Oklahoma" (Taylor 1960).

Habitat—"All specimens in Wisconsin have been found in swales" (Baker 1928). "In nothern Nebraska it was found to be common in drainage ditches and temporary ponds" (Taylor 1960).

LAND GASTROPODS

Family POLYGYRIDAE

Stenotrema leai aliciae (Pilsbry)

Distribution—"Eastern United States from Maryland and Alabama westernward to Kansas and Texas. In Kansas, abundant in eastern half of the state with scattered colonies only in the Plains Border and High Plains geographic provinces" (Leonard 1959).

Habitat—Inhabits moist woodlands and even open areas where protection and moisture are afforded.

Mesodon thyroidus (Say)

Distribution—Eastern North America, from Massachusetts and Ontario west to Minnesota, southwest through Iowa, eastern Nebraska and Kansas to Texas and northern Florida in the east (Leonard 1959).

Habitat—An inhabitant of deep woodlands and flood plains where ample protection is present and moisture conserved.

Family PUPILLIDAE

Gastrocopta pellucida hordeacella (Pilsbry)

Distribution—Southern and Baja California (locally) through southeast Colorado and Kansas to Florida; south to Sinaloa and Tampico, Mexico; north on the Atlantic Coastal Plain to southern New Jersey (Franzen and Leonard 1947; Pilsbry 1948).

Habitat—Taylor (1960) states that this species "may live among the grass roots, occasionally even on exposed slopes. So far as known, the snail has not been collected alive in the Plains."

Remarks—Branson (1961) believes the subspecies *hordeacella* to be "imaginary."

Gastrocopta contracta (Say)

Distribution—"Eastern North America from southern Canada to Florida, west to Manitoba and Texas; Mexico" (Leonard 1959).

Habitat—Occupies a variety of habitats from dense woodlands to open grassland areas.

Gastrocopta armifera (Say)

Distribution—"Eastern North America from southern Canada to northern Florida, west to Alberta, Dakota and New Mexico" (Leonard 1959).

Habitat—Similar to *G. contracta*.

Gastrocopta pentodon (Say)

Distribution—"Eastern North America from southern Canada south to Mexico and central Florida; Guatemala" (Leonard 1950).

Habitat—Occurs "in both wooded areas and under suitable cover in grassland" (Leonard 1959).

Vertigo ovata (Say)

Distribution—"North America from Tigolda and Kodiak Islands, Alaska, and Labrador, south to Florida Keys and West Indies" (Leonard 1959).

Habitat—Usually found with very moist conditions associated with humus, rotting logs and low vegetation; seldom found away from water sources.

Family CARYCHIIDAE

Carychuim exiguum (Say)

Distribution—"Newfoundland to Colorado, south to Mobile Bay, Alabama, and near Deming, southwestern New Mexico" (Pilsbry 1948).

Habitat—Usually associated with moist humus in seepage areas or close to water.

Family CIONELLIDAE

Cionella lubrica (Muller)

Distribution—Holartic, "Point Barrow, Alaska, and Queen Charlotte Islands to Labrador and Newfoundland, south to Washington, D.C., and southern Missouri; in all the western and mountain states except California; to the Mexican boundary in Arizona; in the Sierra Madre of western Chihuahua" (Pilsbry 1948).

Habitat—Usually found under damp humus in dense shade or in rotting logs in thickly wooded areas.

Family ENDODONTIDAE

Helicodiscus parallelus (Say)

Distribution—eastern North America, from Newfoundland south to Georgia and Alabama; westward to South Dakota and Oklahoma (Pilsbry 1948).

Habitat—Usually found in moist areas associated with humus, in grasslands, in stone crevices or other protected areas where moisture is retained.

Helicodiscus singleyanus (Pilsbry)

Distribution—New Jersey to Florida, west to South Dakota, Colorado, and Arizona (Pilsbry 1948).

Habitat—According to Taylor (1960) "this species has apparently never been collected alive in the High Plains." Taylor (1960) speculates that it "lives among grass roots, even on exposed slopes that become hot and dry during the summer."

Discus cronkhitei (Newcomb)

Distribution—Alaska to the mountains of southern California; Rocky Mountains south into Arizona and New Mexico; Colorado and northern Canada east to northern Illinois, Maryland, Newfoundland, and Labrador; also Missouri (Pilsbry 1948).

Habitat—"In the east it lives in humid forest, under dead wood and among rotting leaves or grass in rather wet situations" (Pilsbry 1948). Taylor (1960) states that it "occurred under sticks and logs on moist leaf mold, always close to running water."

Family SUCCINEIDAE

Succinea ovalis Say

Distribution—"Newfoundland and James Bay to North Dakota and Nebraska, south to Alabama" (Pilsbry 1948).

TABLE 2

Species grouped according to habitat preference with total number and percentage given for each species in each of the four collecting sites

Preferred habitat	Species	Waterfall %		NE-IC %		NE-3D %		NE-ID %	
A. Permanent stream with slow to moderate current, several ft. deep.	Valvata tricarinata	3	0.32	9	6.5	5	9.4	14	5.3
	Sphaerium	13	1.4						
	Total %		1.72		6.5		9.4		5.3
B. Shallow, quiet water, one ft. or less, marshy	Promenetus umbilicatellus	1	0.1			1	1.9	1	0.4
	Physa gyrina	64	7.0						
	Physa anatina	25	2.5						
	Gyraulus parvus	337	36.0						
	Lymnaea caperata	6	0.65						
	Pomatiopsis lapidaria	84	9.1	33	23.7	30	56.9	95	38.8
	Total %		55.35		23.7		58.8		39.2
C. Marginal situations near borders of shallow pools	Lymnaea dalli	65	7.0	7	5.1	2	3.7	36	14.6
	Succinea ovalis	23	2.5			1	1.9	1	0.4
	Succinea sp.?	6	0.65	16	11.2			27	10.7
	Total %		10.15		16.3		5.6		25.7
D. Moist situations under humus, usually close to water source	Carychium exiguum	35	3.8	6	4.3	5	9.4	12	4.9
	Gastrocopta pentodon	57	6.2	2	1.4			4	1.6
	Vertigo ovata	16	1.7	8	5.7			6	2.4
	Discus cronkhitei	7	0.75	6	4.3			24	9.7
	Cionella lubrica	1	0.1			3	5.7		
	Total %		12.55		15.7		15.1		18.6
E. Woodland species commonly found in forested areas	Mesodon thyroidus	13	1.4	19	13.3			9	3.7
	Stenotrema leai	70	7.6	4	2.9	3	5.7	2	0.8
	Euconulus fulvus	4	0.43						
	Total %		9.43		16.2		5.7		4.5
F. Protected woodland areas; sparse to thick	Gastrocopta armifera	1	0.1						
	Gastrocopta contracta	4	0.43						
	Strobilops labyrinthica	9	0.97	1	0.7	1	1.9	3	1.2
	Retinella roemeri	2	0.21						
	Retinella electrina	11	1.2	25	18.0	1	1.9	12	4.9
	Retinella indentata	3	0.32	2	1.4	1	1.9		
	Total %		3.23		20.1		5.7		6.1
G. Drought-tolerant species; often requiring little protection	Gastrocopta pellucida hordeacella	7	0.75	1	0.7				
	Hawaiia minuscula	38	4.1					1	0.4
	Vallonia gracilicosta	7	0.75						
	Helicodiscus parrallelus	5	0.54						
	Helicodiscus singleyanus	15	1.6						
	Total %		7.74		0.7				0.4

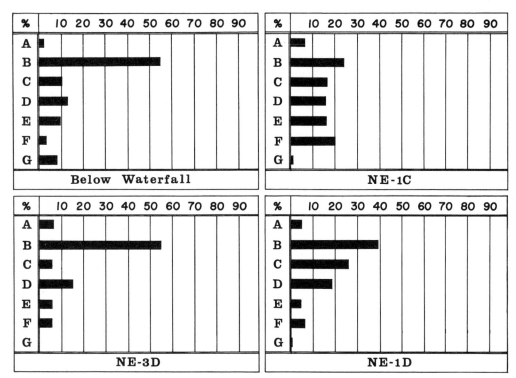

Fig. 32 Graphic representation of Table 2 showing percentage of species representing various habitats for each collecting area. A—permanent stream with slow to moderate current; B— shallow, quiet water; C—borders of shallow pools; D—moist humus close to water; E—forested areas; F—protected woodlands; G—drought tolerant species.

Habitat—"*S. ovalis* is usually found on low ground near streams in summer often upon the weedy herbage of such places, a foot or two from the ground." (Pilsbry, 1948).

Succinea sp.

Although some of the succineid shells collected resembled *S. luteola*, placing these shells in a species would only be a guess. As was pointed out by Miles (1958), with the exception of *Oxyloma retusa, Succinea ovalis* and *Succinea concordialis*, all other species of succineid shells must be identified by the use of soft parts.

Family STROBILOPSIDAE

Strobilops labyrinthica (Say)

Distribution—"Maine and Quebec west to Manitoba, Minnesota, Kansas and Arkansas, south to Georgia and Alabama" (Pilsbry 1948).

Habitat—"Its usual stations are under loose bark of logs, in half-decayed wood, among dead leaves and in sod at bases of trees" (Pilsbry 1948).

Family VALLONIIDAE

Vallonia gracilicosta Reinhardt

Distribution—Minnesota to Montana, south and southwest to Nebraska, New Mexico, Arizona, and California (Pilsbry 1948).

Habitat—"In northern Nebraska this spe-

cies occurs under logs, bark, and stones on slightly moist leaf mold in wooded areas" (Taylor 1960).

Family ZONITIDAE

Euconulus fulvus (Muller)

Distribution—"Almost throughout the Holarctic realm, but wanting in the Gulf and South Atlantic States from Texas to North Carolina" (Pilsbry 1946).

Habitat—"*E. fulvus* lives among damp leaves in well-shaded places, and may usually be obtained by leaf sifting where its presence would otherwise be unsuspected" (Pilsbry 1946).

Retinella electrina (Gould)

Distribution—"North America north of about lat. 38° N., southward in the Rocky Mountains to Arizona and New Mexico" (Taylor 1960).

Habitat—Inhabits "woodlands where it lives in decaying leaves, beneath loosened bark on dead trees and under sticks and fallen logs" (Leonard 1950).

Retinella indentata (Say)

Distribution—"North America from Canada (46° N. Lat.) south to northern Alabama; from Maine west to Kansas" (Leonard 1959).

Habitat—Habitat similar to *R. electrina*.
Retinella roemeri (Pilsbry and Ferriss)
    Distribution—Texas.
    Habitat—Pilsbry (1946) found this species living "in the deeper layers of the debris and dirt near the chalk ledges above the large springs that form most of Comal Creek", New Braunfels, Texas.
Hawaiia minuscula (Binney)
    Distribution—"North America from Alaska and Maine to Costa Rica" (Taylor 1960).
    Habitat—Lives in a variety of habitats and is extremely adaptable. Leonard (1943) states that it "withstands arid conditions successfully but is most numerous in wooded places where moisture conditions are better than on the treeless prairie."

ECOLOGICAL INTERPRETATIONS

Assuming that the preferred habitats of the fossil snails were the same as the preferred habitats of the same species today, then at least seven *preferred* habitats are represented among the thirty species of snails and sphaerids collected. Using these species as paleoecological indicators for the excavation area, the percentages of each species found in each of the seven habitats were calculated in order to ascertain the type of habitat which existed in the Domebo locale. Table 2 summarizes the ecological information in terms of percentages based upon the total shell number for each species in each of the four areas sampled. A graphic interpretation of Table 2 is presented in Figure 32.

It is interesting to note that in all four areas from which shells were collected, the highest percentage fell under the *shallow, quiet water* habitat (B) while the drought-tolerant species (G) constituted the smallest percentage present. The other habitats represented would indicate standing pools of water, surrounding woodlands and abundant moist humus.

Judging from these data, the area in which the mammoth was found was probably a stream or spring-fed marsh with a luxuriant growth of vegetation. Surrounding the marsh was woodland varying from sparse to dense. Considering the shell-size of *L. caperata* (many reaching a length of 20 mm.), *P. gyrina* (prevalent, with many shells 18 mm. long), and *L. dalli* (some 6.5 mm. long), growth conditions were apparently at the optimum for these species. *S. leai* and *P. lapidaria* also indicate greater moisture in the area than there is today for these species thrive best in broad-leaf deciduous tree zones where the annual rainfall varies from 30 to 60 inches. The southern geographical range of *H. singleyanus* and *G. pellucida hordeacella*, which are seldom found living north of the 42° parallel, can be used to indicate a relatively mild winter climate.

Sub-freezing temperatures (if encountered) would have been of short duration. On the other hand the presence of *V. tricarinata*, *P. umbili catellus*, *D. cronkhitei* and *L. caperata* which seldom range to the south of the 35° parallel would indicate the absence of the seasonable high temperatures which occur in Oklahoma today.

Radiocarbon dates of 10,123±280 and 11,045±637 for the lower member of the Domebo Formation indicate a late Wisconsin age. However, it must be pointed out that without the C-14 dates, the availability of vertebrate remains or stratigraphic evidence, it would be difficult, if not impossible, to indicate a distinct Wisconsin, Illinoian or Sangamonian age. Because of the close climatic similarities of periods within these stages they cannot be distinguished on the basis of shells alone. Climatically, each presented an environment which would probably have been favorable to all of the amphibious mollusks reported in this paper.

REFERENCES CITED

ALLEN, DON AND E. P. CHEATUM
  1961a A Pleistocene Molluscan Fauna Near Byers, Clay County, Texas. *Journal of the Graduate Research Center*, Vol. 29, No. 3. Dallas.
  1961b Ecological Implications of Fresh-Water and Land Gastropods in Texas Archeological Studies. *Bulletin of the Texas Archeological Society*, Vol. 31. Austin.

BAKER, F. C.
  1909 Mollusks from Kansas and Oklahoma. *Nautilus*, Vol. 23. Philadelphia.
  1928 The Freshwater Mollusca of Wisconsin. Part I: Gastropoda. *Wisconsin Academy of Science, Arts and Letters Bulletin* 70. Madison.

BRANSON, A. BRANLEY
  1959 The Recent Gastropoda of Oklahoma, Part 1, Historical Review, General Comments and Higher Taxonomic Categories. *Proceedings of the Oklahoma Academy of Science*, Vol. 39. Stillwater.
  1961a Recent Gastropoda of Oklahoma, Part 2. *Biological Studies Series No. 6*, Oklahoma State University. Stillwater.
  1961b The Recent Gastropoda of Oklahoma, Part 3: Terrestrial Species: Pupillidae, Carychiidae, Strobilopsidae and Oligyridae. *Proceedings of the Oklahoma Academy of Science*, Vol 41. Stillwater.

FERRISS, J. H.
  1900 In Search of *Polygyra pilsbryi*. *Nautilus*, Vol. 14. Philadelphia.
  1906 Mollusks of Oklahoma. *Nautilus*, Vol 20. Philadelphia.

FRAZEN, D.
  1946 A new Fossil Pupillid. *Nautilus*, Vol. 20. Philadelphia.
  1947 Living and Fossil Pupillidae (Gastropoda) of the Sanborn Area, Northwestern Kansas. *Transactions of the Kansas Academy of Science*, No. 49, Lawrence.

FRANZEN, D. S. AND A. B. LEONARD.
  1947 Fossil and Living Pupillidae (Gastropoda, Pulmonata) in Kansas. *University of Kansas Science Bulletin*, No. 31. Lawrence.

FRYE, J. C. AND A. B. LEONARD
    1952   Pleistocene Geology of Kansas. *Kansas Geological Survey Bulletin 99*, Lawrence.

GREGER, D. K.
    1915   The Gastropods of Payne County, Oklahoma. *Nautilus*, Vol. 29. Philadelphia.

HERRINGTON, H. B.
    1962   A Revision of the Sphaeriidae of North America (Mollusca: Pelecypoda). *Miscellaneous Publications of the Museum of Zoology, University of Michigan*, No. 118. Ann Arbor.

HIBBARD, C. W.
    1949a   Techniques of Collecting Microvertebrate Fossils. *Contributions of the Museum of Paleontology, University of Michigan*, Vol. 8. Ann Arbor.
    1949b   Pleistocene Vertebrate Paleontology in North America. *In* Pleistocene Research: A Review by the Members of the Committee on Interrelations of Pleistocene Research, National Research Council. *Bulletin of the Geological Society of America*, Vol 60. Baltimore.

HIBBARD, C. W. AND D. W. TAYLOR
    1960   Two Late Pleistocene Faunas from Southwestern Kansas. *Contributions of the Museum of Paleontology, University of Michigan*, Vol. 16. Ann Arbor.

ISELY, F. B.
    1924   The Freshwater Mussel Fauna of Eastern Oklahoma. *Proceedings of the Oklahoma Academy of Science*, Vol. 4. Stillwater.

LEONARD, A. B.
    1950   A Yarmouthian Molluscan Fauna in the Mid-Continent Region of the United States. *Kansas University Paleontological Contributions*, No. 8. Lawrence.
    1959   Handbook of Gastropods in Kansas. *University of Kansas Miscellaneous Publications*, No. 20. Lawrence.

LEONARD, A. B. AND D. S. FRANZEN
    1944   Mollusca of the Laverne Formation (Lower Pliocene) of Beaver County, Oklahoma. *University of Kansas Science Bulletin*, Vol. 30. Lawrence.
    1946   A Review of the Genus Calipyrgula Pilsbry (Gastropoda: Amnicolidae). *University of Kansas Science Bulletin*, Vol. 31. Lawrence.

MILES, C. D.
    1958   The Family Succineidae (Gastropoda: Pulmonata) in Kansas. *University of Kansas Science Bulletin*, Vol. 38. Lawrence.

PILSBRY, H. A.
    1899   New Southwestern Forms of Polygyra. *Nautilus*, Vol. 13. Philadelphia.
    1902   Southwestern Land Snails. *Proceedings of the Philadelphia Academy of Natural Science*. Philadelphia.
    1903   Mollusca of Western Arkansas and Adjacent States with a Revision of Paravitrea. *Proceedings of the Philadelphia Academy of Natural Science*. Philadelphia.
    1939   Land Mollusca of North America (North of Mexico). *Monographs of the Philadelphia Academy of Natural Science*, Vol. 1, No. 3, Pt. 1. Philadelphia.
    1940   Land Mollusca of North America (North of Mexico). *Monographs of the Philadelphia Academy of Natural Science*, Vol. 1, No. 3, Pt. 2. Philadelphia.
    1946   Land Mollusca of North America (North of Mexico). *Monographs of the Philadelphia Academy of Natural Science*, Vol. 2, No. 3, Pt. 1. Philadelphia.
    1948   Land Mollusca of North America (North of Mexico). *Monographs of the Philadelphia Academy of Natural Science*, Vol. 3, No. 3, Pt. 2. Philadelphia.

PILSBRY, H. A. AND J. H. FERRISS
    1906   Mollusca of the Ozarkian Fauna. *Proceedings of the Philadelphia Academy of Natural Science*, Vol. 58. Philadelphia.

SIMPSON, C. J.
    1888   Notes on Some Indian Territory Land and Fresh Water Shells. *Proceedings of the U.S. National Museum*, Vol. 2. Washington, D.C.

TAYLOR, D. W.
    1954   A New Pleistocene Fauna and New Species of Fossil Snails from the High Plains. *University of Michigan, Occasional Publications of the Museum of Zoology*, No. 557. Ann Arbor.
    1960   Late Cenozoic Molluscan Faunas from the High Plains. *U. S. Geologic Survey Professional Paper No. 337*. Washington, D.C.

TAYLOR, D. W. AND C. W. HIBBARD
    1955   A New Pleistocene Fauna from Harper County, Oklahoma. *Oklahoma Geological Survey Circular 37*. Norman.

WALKER, B.
    1909   Notes on Planorbis, Part II: *P. bicarinatus*. *Nautilus*, Vol. 23. Philadelphia.
    1915   A list of Shells Collected in Arizona, New Mexico, Texas and Oklahoma by Dr. E. L. Case. *University of Michigan, Occasional Publications of the Museum of Zoology*, No. 15. Ann Arbor.

PALYNOLOGY OF THE DOMEBO SITE

L. R. Wilson

THE DISCOVERY several years ago by Mr. J. E. Patterson of a buried mammoth skeleton three miles east of Stecker in Caddo County, Oklahoma, led to a cooperative scientific study by several investigators under the auspices of the Museum of the Great Plains at Lawton, Oklahoma. This paper is a report of one of those studies. Appreciation is here expressed to Mr. Marvin E. Tong, Jr., Mr. Adrian D. Anderson, and Mr. Frank C. Leonhardy of the Museum of the Great Plains for aiding in the investigation and the publication of the report. Dr. C. C. Branson, State Geologist of Oklahoma, assisted with the collection of palynological samples, and appreciation is expressed.

The mammoth skeleton was found buried in a blue-black clay deposit approximately four feet thick, near the bottom of an actively eroding stream valley, the Domebo Branch of Tonkawa Creek. The locality of the Domebo site is reported as in the NE¼, SW¼, SE¼, Sec. 29, T. 6 N., R. 10 W., Tonkawa Town, Caddo County, Oklahoma.

The stratigraphic section exposed in the eastern bank of the creek where the mammoth skeleton was found can be divided into two sections: the basal portion consisting of a brownish sandy layer that is approximately four feet thick, and a bluish clay, 37 inches thick, which contained the skeleton. Above the bluish clay the predominant sediment is a buff sand which is, in part, laminated toward the top. The upper section is approximately thirty-two feet thick. The relationship of the beds is shown in Figures 11 and 35. A more detailed description of the stratigraphy is given by Albritton in this symposium.

The "blue clay" layer is widely distributed in Oklahoma, and because it generally contains a palynological flora, it became of special interest when discovered in the Domebo site. In addition to containing an extinct large mammal and artifacts, two stumps of trees were found *in situ*, and the radiocarbon date of one was determined. Seldom do so many important finds occur together. The overlying sands which constitute the upper part of the section unfortunately have not yielded satisfactory palynological assemblages. Although many fossil spores and pollen occur in the "blue clay" samples, they have not been preserved as well as one would desire them to be. Photomicrographs have been made of the best specimens that illustrate diagnostic features. However, some fossils reported could not be satisfactorily photographed and do not appear in Figure 36.

SAMPLE COLLECTIONS AND PREPARATION

The site was visited on March 9, 1962, during the excavation of the mammoth skeleton, and, with the aid of Mr. Adrian Anderson and Dr. C. C. Branson, palynological samples were collected. Samples were taken from the clays associated with the mammoth bones, and a channel sample of seven segments was collected from below the level of the skeleton upward to the top of the "blue clay." The location and thicknesses of these collections are shown in Figure 35.

The samples were cut from a freshly cleaned exposure and were placed in collecting bags for transport to the laboratory. There they were air dried, pulverized, and mixed before being split for preparation and analysis. Samples weighing approximately twenty grams were placed in separate jars with 5 cc. of Calgon detergent and one pint of distilled water. The jars were agitated for eight hours to disassociate the spores and pollen from the clays. After settling, excess water was siphoned off and the organic clay residue put in polyethylene beakers.

Dilute hydrochloric acid was then poured over the sample to remove any calcium carbonate prior to its treatment with hydrofluoric acid. When the hydrochloric acid had ceased its reaction, distilled water was added to the sample and the sediment allowed to settle. The excess water was removed by siphoning or centrifuging and the sample was covered with several times its volume of 52 per cent hydrofluoric acid. This acid is especially dangerous and should not be used by anyone unfamiliar with its properties. Generally eight to twelve hours are necessary for the digestion of the silica particles in the samples, and then they may be diluted with distilled water, centrifuged, and washed several times. When the samples are free of hydrofluoric acid and neutral, they may be examined under the microscope for palynological materials. Commonly no further processing is necessary, but the Domebo site samples required additional treatment with Schulze's solution (1 part potassium chlorate and 5 parts concentrated nitric acid) to separate the spores and pollen. This technique generally requires four to eight hours for maceration. Upon completion of digestion, distilled water is added and the sediment allowed to settle. The excess solution is decanted and the sediment is washed with distilled water and centrifuged until neutral. If, upon examination with the microscope, the spores and pollen are still black, the sample can be placed in a 10 percent potassium hydroxide solution for a few minutes and then washed with distilled water until neutral. The Domebo samples required the potassium hydroxide treatment and at that step

the stain, Safranin O, was added. After repeated washing and centrifuging of the samples, microscope slides were made. The mountant used was Clearcol, a water-miscible mounting medium, and the seal was Harleco (Wilson, 1959). The photomicrographs illustrating this paper were taken with the Zeiss Photomicroscope, using Adox KB14 film.

The palynological assemblages reported in the histograms (Fig. 35) have been determined from counts of two hundred to five hundred specimens and computed to the nearest percent. Generally the procedure has been to count 25 fossils from each slide rather than to attempt a total count from one. In this manner a more uniform sampling of the assemblage is obtained.

PALYNOLOGICAL ASSEMBLAGE

The two most abundant pollen types in the Domebo section are grasses (Gramineae) and composites (Compositae). These are predominantly air-borne (anemophilous) pollen grains, and, because of their relative small sizes, except for some of the grasses, they are preserved in more environments than are the larger and more delicate grains. Amaranth (Amaranthaceae) and chenopod (Chenopodiaceae) grains combined constitute the third important group in the prairie flora. Their pollen grains are similar to the grasses in pollination habit and preservation character. Conifer pollen occurs almost

FIG. 33 View of prairie west from Domebo Canyon showing the typical tall grass and Compositae vegetation and the extension of the forest into the prairie by way of the canyon.

FIG. 34   Location of Domebo site of east bank of Domebo Branch. The mammoth skeleton was excavated from the position where the figure on the left is standing. The section studied for palynology is shown to the rear.

throughout the section, and also in some of the finer sediments above the "blue clay," which are otherwise barren, and in the leaf litter of the top soil (Sample T) at the valley edge. Because there are no native pine or spruce trees within the region today, and because pine (*Pinus*) and spruce (*Picea*) pollen occur in the leaf litter of the top soil in approximately the same abundance as lower in the section, it is assumed that most, if not all, of these pollen grains were transported by wind from coniferous regions to the west. Conifer pollen appears to be among the most decay-resistant types and is commonly found in palynological preparations that are barren of all other types.

Many spore and pollen types occur only as single specimens, and many of these are presently not identifiable because they are either poorly preserved or they belong to difficult taxonomic groups. Because their abundance is approximately uniform throughout the section, they were not used in Figure 35.

In the initial stage of sample preparation an investigation was made for diatom fossils because these plants are present in the Domebo Branch today. Soil samples were washed in distilled water and studied as wet mounts, but diatoms were not discovered in any preparations. It is possible that these organisms were present at the time of the sediment deposition but have been dissolved by slightly alkaline ground water.

An abundance of fungus spores are present in the preparations. These, for the most part, are soil fungus types characteristic of swampy environments. One form, *Rhizophagites* (Rosendahl, 1943; Wilson, 1965) is abundant in the region today and has a fossil record extending from Nebraskan time to the present. The number of fungal spores far outnumber the total of all other palynological fossils. Because fungus spores do not necessarily indicate the regional flora, they have not been reported in the relative assemblage population.

Although the palynology of the Domebo site is primarily concerned with Pleistocene and Recent floras, there occur, associated with the Pleistocene fossils in the "blue clay," numerous Permian spores which have been redeposited or recycled from the Rush Springs Sandstone. This type of phenomenon is widely recognized, and the recycled fossils give information concerning the source of the sediments from which they were derived.

PALEOECOLOGY

Pleistocene and near-Recent biotas are generally compared with the extant biota in the same area in order to draw comparisons. For this reason a general vegetational inspection was made of the Domebo Branch area on August 19, 1964. The following plant communities were observed:

UPLAND

Adjacent to Domebo Branch valley a longgrass prairie vegetation dominates as shown in Figure 33. Studies of this vegetational type have been made in the nearby Wichita Mountains

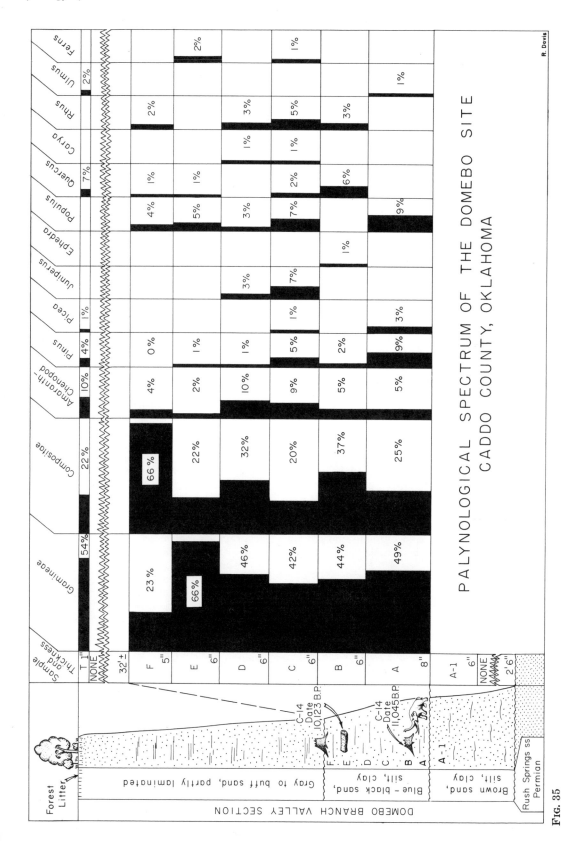

PALYNOLOGICAL SPECTRUM OF THE DOMEBO SITE
CADDO COUNTY, OKLAHOMA

R. Davis

FIG. 35

47

Wildlife Refuge by Eskew (1938), Buck (1962), and Crockett (1962), and essentially the same conditions and flora are present near the valley of Domebo Branch. Although grasses, especially blue stem (*Andropogon*), are dominant in the ecological assemblage, there is an abundance of composite and amaranth species belonging to the genera *Veronia*, *Rudbeckia*, and *Amaranthus*. Intruding into the prairie communities by way of the intermittent stream valleys are small trees of blackjack oak (*Quercus marilandica*), chestnut oak (*Q. muehlenbergii*), hackberry (*Celtis occidentalis* var. *canina*), and juniper (*Juniperus* sp.). The prickly-pear cactus (*Opuntia* sp.) is locally abundant.

THE VALLEY AND EDGES OF DOMEBO BRANCH

The vegetation in the valley and on the edges of Domebo Branch are in sharp contrast to the Prairie-Plains into which it extends. Mature trees of American elm (*Ulmus americana*), chestnut oak, and black oak (*Quercus velutina* var. *missouriensis*) are common and form an upper canopy of branches under which grow smaller trees of hawthorn (*Crataegus* sp.), wild plum (*Prunus* sp.), redbud (*Cercis canadensis*), dogwood (*Cornus* sp.), and juniper (*Juniperus virginiana*). On the valley sides, where not completely shaded, grow shrubs of sumac (*Rhus glabra*) and thickets of greenbriar (*Smilax* sp.). Lianas, such as grape (*Vitis* sp.) and Virginia creeper (*Parthenocissus quinquefolia*), are locally abundant. The stream bed and banks are populated with willows (*Salix* sp.), poison ivy (*Rhus radicans*), scouring rush (*Equisetum prealtum*), grasses, sedges, and other herbaceous plants. In the deepest shade, generally in the shelter of a steep bank, are found mosses of the genus *Mnium* and the fragile fern (*Asplenium fragilis*).

DISCUSSION

It is important to note that, with respect to the fossil pollen assemblages, cottonwood (*Populus deltoides*) is rare in the present plant community near the Domebo site and pine (*Pinus*) does not grow in this part of the state. The pinon pine (*Pinus edulis*) is known from the Edwards Plateau in Kerr County, Texas, and from the Black Mesa area in Cimarron County, Oklahoma. The western yellow pine also occurs in the Black Mesa area, but these pine-forest localities are several hundred miles to the west and northwest of the Domebo Site. In the east and southeastern parts of Oklahoma other pine species occur, but these are even more distant from the Domebo site.

The palynological histograms (Fig. 35) indicate the plant successional trends which took place over a period of more than one thousand years. It appears possible that, by comparing the fossil assemblages with the palynological assemblage from the surface soil litter (Sample T), the paleoecology of the period between 11,-500 and 9,000 or 10,000 years ago may be interpreted with some accuracy.

The general palynological assemblage from the "blue clay" is dominated by grass and composite pollen from bottom to top. The bottom sample in the clay, which was collected from a fill associated with the mammoth bones, contains more pine and spruce pollen than samples higher in the section. Initially this condition was interpreted as indicating more boreal conditions, but, with the discovery of similar conifer pollen grains in the surface litter (Sample T), the validity of such an interpretation was questioned. Rainwater pollen studies made at Norman, Oklahoma, before the local pine trees were shedding pollen, show that large quantities of this and other types of pollen occur in the samples, which must be interpreted as being transported by air masses from the southern and western parts of the country. The fact that pine constitutes less than nine percent and spruce less than three percent of the fossil pollen spectrum is sufficient reason to question the existence of pine or spruce in the vicinity of the Domebo site when the "blue clay" was being deposited. When pine occurs in a region, its relative abundance in a pollen sample is in the magnitude of 50 to 90 percent. Sample "B" contained several pollen grains of *Ephedra*, a genus limited to desert or semi-desert habitats and is represented in southwestern Oklahoma by only one species. *Ephedra* pollen, like pine pollen, is known to be wind transported far beyond its geographic range, consequently it is of no certain ecological significance in the Domebo spectrum.

The occurrence of oak (*Quercus*), hickory (*Carya*), and possibly some of the herbaceous pollen in the spectrum suggests that from the time of deposition of sample "B" through that of sample "D" a plant succession toward a more closed wooded valley took place. It is also worthy to note that sample "A" contained two grains of elm (*Ulmus*) pollen. This is the level of the mammoth skeleton and of a stump identified by the Forest Products Laboratory in Madison, Wisconsin, as similar to the winged elm (*Ulmus alata*). However, a great extension of woodland into the prairie is not indicated because of the predominant abundance of grass, amaranth-chenopod, and composite pollen in the spectrum. The occurrence of a marked change in relative abundance of grass and composite pollen in levels "E" and "F" may suggest that an ecological change took place in the regional prairie. Grass pollen in sample "E" is 66 per-

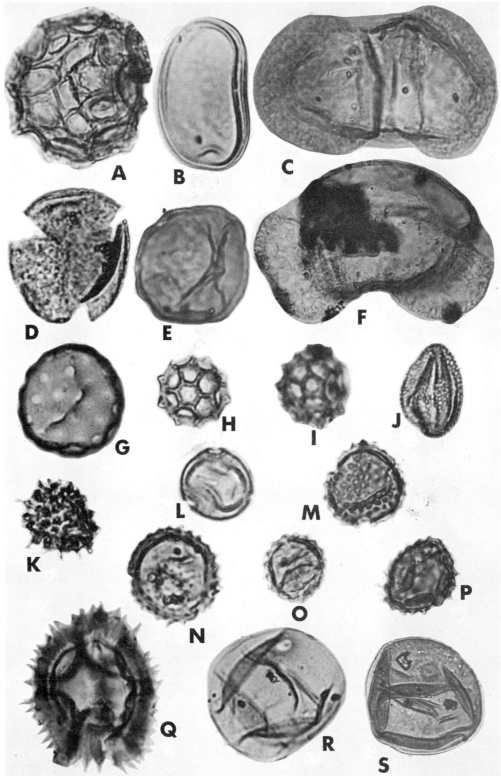

FIG. 36 Spores and pollen from the Domebo site. A—fungus spore; B—fern spore; C—*Picea* sp.; D—*Quercus* sp.; E—*Ulmus* sp.; F—*Pinus* sp.; G—*Chenopodium* sp.; H, I—*Amaranthus* sp.; J—Tricolpate pollen; K—Compositae pollen; L—Triporate pollen; M to Q—Compositae pollen; R, S—Graminae pollen.

cent of the assemblage and composite pollen is 22 percent, but in sample "F" the assemblage is almost the opposite—grass pollen is 23 percent and composite pollen is 66 percent. The change in pollen dominance may have resulted from factors also reflected in the change of sedimentation from "blue clay" to the gray and buff sand that overlies level "F."

The similarity between the pollen spectra from the "blue clay" levels and the surface soil litter gives a definite impression that the paleoecological conditions at the Domebo site in the Late Pleistocene were much like modern ecological conditions. However, the abundantly dispersed organic matter which gives the lower Domebo sediments their distinctive blue-black color probably indicates that the sediments were formed under conditions more humid than at present because the slack water deposits being formed today do not contain nearly so much organic matter and are mostly red. ∧

REFERENCES CITED

BUCK, PAUL
 1962   Relationships of the Woody Vegetation of the Wichita Mountains Wildlife Refuge to Geological Formations and Soil Types. Unpublished Ph.D. dissertation, University of Oklahoma, Norman.

CROCKETT, J. J.
 1962   Grassland Communities of the Wichita Mountains Wildlife Refuge. Unpublished Ph.D. dissertation, University of Oklahoma, Norman.

ESKEW, C. T.
 1938   The Flowering Plants of the Wichita Mountains Wildlife Refuge. *American Midland Naturalist*, Vol. 20. Notre Dame.

ROSENDAHL, C. O.
 1948   A Contribution to the Knowledge of the Pleistocene Flora of Minnesota. *Ecology*, Vol. 29. Durham.

WILSON, L. R.
 1959   A Water-Miscible Mountant for Palynology. *Geology Notes*, Vol. 19. Oklahoma Geological Survey, Norman.

 1965   *Rhizophagites*, a Fossil Fungus from the Pleistocene of Oklahoma. *Geology Notes*, Vol. 25. Oklahoma Geological Survey, Norman.

LATE PLEISTOCENE RESEARCH AT DOMEBO:
A SUMMARY AND INTERPRETATION

Frank C. Leonhardy

SOMETIME PRIOR to 11,200 years ago sediments began to accumulate in a marsh at the bottom of Domebo Canyon. On the basis of radiocarbon dates these marsh sediments, the lower member of the Domebo Formation, may be correlated with the Sulphur River Formation (Slaughter and Hoover 1963) which, in turn, has been correlated with the Holloway Prairie Formation of the Gulf Coast (Doering 1963). The Holloway Prairie Formation marks a period of rising sea level, which would have resulted in a period of aggradation in the Red River system, including the Washita River to which Domebo Branch is ultimately tributary. Such an aggrading situation would account for the presence of a slack water embayment in the canyon, at least during parts of the year.

The boundary between the upper and lower members of the Domebo Formation marks a radical change from slack water settling to sheet and rill deposition, but the mechanism of the change is still unknown. It could be related to a change in the regimen of the master stream or it could signify nothing more than the establishment of a graded bed along the upper reaches of the creek. The date of the change in the mode of deposition would be of some importance, but it cannot yet be fixed with certainty. In Domebo Canyon and in other canyons where analogous deposits occur, bones of *Bison bison* and artifacts of Archaic and Late Prehistoric types occur in the sandy upper members. Thus, the date of the depositional change is sometime between 10,000 B.P., the minimum terminal date for the lower member of the Domebo Formation, and 6,000 B.P., the earliest Archaic data thus far obtained in the region (Bastian 1964).

Comparison of the chronology of the lower member of the Domebo Formation with glacial events in the Lake Michigan area as reviewed by Broecker and Farrand (1963) indicates that deposition of the lower member began about the time of the maximum advance of the ice during the Valders stade and that most of the deposit would be contemporaneous with the early phase of the Valders recession. No causality is implied, but this seems striking, especially in view of the probable correlation with the Holloway Prairie Formation and a period of rising sea level.

Ecological and climatological data recovered from the Domebo locale exhibit a high degree of internal consistency. Further, the conclusions derived from these data are consistent with paleoecological and paleoclimatological reconstructions for neighboring north central Texas and the Llano Estacado.

Information derived from the molluscan and vertebrate faunas indicates one basic difference between modern climate and the Late Wisconsin climate of 10,000 to 11,500 years ago. The climate then was probably more moderate. The presence of the cotton rat, *Sigmodon hispidus,* the tortoise *Geochelone wilsoni*, the extinct box turtle *Terrapene carolina putnami* and the mollusks *Helicodiscus singleyanus* and *Gastrocopta pellusida* is interpreted as indicating winters without prolonged periods of freezing temperatures. The sympatric bog lemming, *Synaptomys cooperi*, and the mollusks *Valvata tricarinata*, *Promenetus umbilicatellus*, *Discus cronkhitei* and *Limnaea caperata* are indicative of cooler summer temperatures.

The conclusions based on the limited Domebo fauna are reinforced by comparison with two contemporary faunas from nearby areas: The Ben Franklin local fauna, Delta County, Texas (Slaughter and Hoover 1963), and the Brown Sand Wedge local fauna from Blackwater Locality No. 1 near Clovis, New Mexico (Slaughter, n.d.). Both of these Faunas have additional members, the meadow vole, *Microtus pennsylvanicus,* and the masked shrew, *Sorex cinerus*, which indicate cooler summers. *Synaptomys cooperi* is also represented in the Ben Franklin fauna. The present southern limit of the ranges of these three species corresponds closely to the 72° mean summer isotherm (see Slaughter and Hoover 1963, Fig. 3).

Sympatric species indicative of mild winters are the cotton rat, *Sigmodon hispidus*, and the beautiful armadillo, *Dasypus bellus*, in the Ben Franklin fauna and the voles *Microtus mexicanus* and *M. ochrogaster*, *Sigmodon hispidus*, *Dasypus bellus*, *Geochelone wilsoni* and *Terrapene carolina putnami* in the Brown Sand Wedge fauna. The occurrence of two extinct turtles, *G. wilsoni* and *T. c. putnami*, in both the Brown Sand Wedge and the Domebo faunas is an interesting feature, for their closest living relatives are tropical and sub-tropical forms. The mollusks used as climatic parameter indicators at Domebo which were found in the Ben Franklin fauna are *Discus cronkhitei*, *Lymnaea caperata* and *Valvata tricarinata*.

The presence of any one of the animals used as indicators of climatic parameters is not necessarily conclusive, for factors other than temperature or moisture could account for the presence of an individual species. In the three faunas discussed, however, there are recurrent constellations of species which give greater weight to conclusions regarding climate derived from any one fauna.

There is no direct way of computing the Late Pleistocene temperatures from the available data. Some of the animals present in the three faunas are currently distributed north of the 72° mean summer isotherm, so, all other factors being equal, the average summer temperature during Domebo time may have been about the same or less. This means that the average July high temperatures would have been at least 4° cooler and, depending on how far south the 72° mean summer isotherm was, the temperatures could have been as much as 10° cooler.

Simply on the basis of *a priori* reasoning, one might expect more available moisture during the Late Wisconsin than there is at present as a function of reduced evaporation brought about by cooler summers. There seems to be no direct evidence of greater precipitation in the data, however. The abundant humic material in the lower member and in other contemporary slack water deposits is interpreted as indicative of a more luxuriant vegetation and, hence, more available moisture. The abundance of molluscan species which require moist vegetation and humus supports such an interpretation. The abundance of aquatic species is more difficult to interpret, for their presence is a result of the marsh and the marsh could have formed through factors other than greater rainfall.

On the basis of the Ben Franklin faunas Slaughter and Hoover (1963:144) postulated more available moisture in north central Texas during the Late Wisconsin than there is at present. In the Brown Sand Wedge fauna several species indicate that there must have been as much moisture in the vicinity of Blackwater Draw as there was in the vicinity of Domebo and the Sulphur River. The prairie vole, *Microtus ochrogaster*, probably indicates the presence of tall grass prairie and the red fox, tree squirrel and black bear are indicative of the presence of trees in the vicinity, at least in the valley. Further, none of the arid-land species such as the kangaroo rat and grasshopper mouse, which are abundant in the Blackwater Draw region today, are represented in the Brown Sand Wedge fauna.

Reeves (1965a) computed the mean monthly and mean annual temperatures and evaporation rates for the Llano Estacado during Cary time from a combination of factors. His initial results indicated an 18° F. depresson in the July highs, which, presuming no difference in the average January temperatures, resulted in a reduction of approximately 50 percent in the evaporation rate. This and subsequent studies (Reeves 1965b) show by various methods that late Pleistocene precipitation in the southern Plains must have averaged thirty-three to thirty-six inches. These studies, it should be emphasized, are for the period of the Cary stade which is earlier than the marsh deposits at Domebo. The reduction of temperature during the later Valders time need not have been so great in order to account for the presence of species not present in the southern Plains today. On the basis of diatoms and mollusks Wendorf (1961, Fig. 44) postulated summers at least 10° cooler than today in the Llano Estacado during a period contemporary with the Domebo fauna.

The data and comparisons seem to indicate that not only was the Late Wisconsin climate more moderate than today, but that climatic conditions were more uniform throughout the southern Plains. Present climatic conditions, particularly temperature and rainfall, vary radically from east to west across this region, and to account for the apparent differences between modern and Late Wisconsin climatic conditions involves factors well beyond the scope of this paper.

Paleobotanical data for the Domebo locale indicate a situation very similar to that of today: a humid woodland limited to the bottom and slopes of the valley and a surrounding prairie grassland. The pollen spectrum does indicate a somewhat greater forest cover in the canyon during the deposition of the lower member.

otherwise, there is no great difference in the vegetation of modern and Late Wisconsin times. The most recent climatic reconstruction for the Southern High Plains, a brief review by Oldfield and Schoenwetter (1964, Fig. 1) places the era of the Llano Complex at the boundary of the White Lake Interval and the Lubbock subpluvial, a period marked by a vegetation change from "pine parkland" to "pine woodland." Such a change in vegetation is indicative of cooler temperature and increased moisture and supports Slaughter's contention that there must have been at least some forest in the vicinity of Blackwater Draw at the time of the Brown Sand Wedge fauna. At the moment, however, we hesitate to carry the comparison of the Domebo data and the Llano Estacado reconstruction too far, for Wendorf (personal communciation) informs us that the chronology of the vegetation changes and the pluvial sequences is still in flux. Further, the chronology of cultural materials shown in the chart of Oldfield and Schoenwetter is at variance with information, principally radiocarbon dates, available for this study.

The basic differences in Late Wisconsin plant communities between the Llano Estacado and the Prairie-Plains is likely a function of altitude. While there is no evidence of the presence of pine and spruce in the Prairie-Plains during Valders time, there is abundant conifer pollen in the Llano Estacado profiles. The available descriptions of distribution of woodland on the Llano during this period are somewhat confusing. Hafsten (1961, Fig. 34) describes the vegetation as "primarily grassland but boreal woodlands in favorable locations," but the review of Oldfield and Schoenwetter does not actually specify the distribution of forest. Hafsten's description is the more consistent with the conclusions based on the data from Domebo.

The principal archaeological significance of the Domebo site is that the Clovis point-mammoth association extends the distribution of the Llano Complex to the eastern margin of the southern Great Plains. There is also the admittedly tenuous evidence linking the Clovis and Plainview projectile point types.

On the basis of observations on projectile points, Leonhardy (1965) postulated that most of the Paleo-Indian complexes in western Oklahoma are manifestations of the Llano, Folsom and Plainview complexes which are best known from the southern High Plains. If the conclusions regarding Late Pleistocene climate and ecology in the southern Plains are reasonably accurate and if, in particular, there was a greater similarity between the southern High Plains and the southern Prairie-Plains than there is today, then it is possible to view the entire region as one large ecological sphere which supported the game exploited by the Paleo-Indian. The overriding cultural pattern was the hunting of the Pleistocene megafauna, and it is this pattern, as much as similarities in artifacts, that implies a cultural unity throughout the region. ⋀

REFERENCES CITED

BASTIAN, TYLER
  1964 Radiocarbon Date for an Archaic Site in Southwestern Oklahoma. *Oklahoma Anthropological Society Newsletter*, Vol. 12, No. 9. Norman.

BROECKER, WALLACE S. AND WILLIAM R. FARRAND
  1963 Radiocarbon Age of the Two Creeks Forest Bed, Wisconsin. *Bulletin of the Geological Society of America*, Vol. 74. Baltimore.

CHEATUM, E. P. AND DON ALLEN
  1963 An Ecological comparison of the Ben Franklin and Clear Creek Local Molluscan Faunas in Texas. *Journal of the Graduate Research Center*, Vol. 31, No. 3. Dallas.

DOERING, JOHN A.
  1963 Correlation of the Sulphur River Formation. *Journal of the Graduate Research Center*, Vol. 31, No. 3. Dallas.

HAFSTEN, ULF
  1961 Pleistocene Development of Vegetation and Climate in the Southern High Plains as Evidenced by Pollen Analysis. In *Paleoecology of the Llano Estacado*, No. 1, assembled by Fred Wendorf. Fort Burgwin Research Center, Taos.

LEONHARDY, FRANK C.
  1965 Prehistoric Occupation in Southwestern Oklahoma, Part I: Paleo-Indian and Archaic. Paper read at the Thirtieth Annual Meeting of the Society for American Archaeology, Urbana, Illinois. MS.

OLDFIELD, FRANK, AND JAMES SCHOENWETTER
  1964 Late Quaternary Environments and Early Man on the Southern High Plains. *Antiquity*, Vol. 38, No. 151 Cambridge.

REEVES, C. C.
  1965a Pleistocene Climate of the Llano Estacado. *Journal of Geology*, Vol. 73, No. 1. Chicago.
  1965b Pluvial Lakes and Pleistocene Climate on the Southern Plains. *Great Plains Journal*, Vol. 5, No. 1. Lawton.

SLAUGHTER, BOB H.
  n.d. An Ecological Interpretation of the Brown Sand Wedge Local Fauna, Blackwater Draw, New Mexico, and a Hypothesis Concerning Late Pleistocene Extinction. "Preprint from *Paleoecology of the Llano Estacado*, Vol. 2, assembled by Fred Wendorf and J. J. Hester." Mimeo.

SLAUGHTER, BOB H. AND B. REED HOOVER
  1963 Sulphur River Formation and the Pleistocene Mammals of the Ben Franklin Local Fauna. *Journal of the Graduate Research Center*, Vol. 31, No. 3. Dallas.

Composed, printed and bound by Semco Color Press, Oklahoma City.

Text of the book is set in 8, 10 and 12 point Bodoni Book, display lines are set in 14 and 18 point Melior Bold.

Body printed on Moistrite Vellum Offset. Cover stock is Ripple Hammermill.

Cover design by Hendrik Martin Van Duiker of Semco Color Press.

Book design by Hendrik Martin Van Duiker and Frank Leonhardy.